A
RADICAL
INCARNATION

The President of the United States Becomes Enlightened,
Heals America and Awakens Humanity —
A Spiritual Fantasy

COLIN C. TIPPING

Award Winning Author of
RADICAL Forgiveness,
Making Room for the Miracle

"A RADICAL INCARNATION"

Published in April, 2003

ISBN **0-9704814-2-X**

Global 13 Publications, Inc.
26 Briar Gate Lane,
Marietta GA 30066
Website: www.radicalforgiveness.com

Cover Design: Deborah Hill
Illustrations: JoAnna Tipping
Editing: Diana Urbas

Disclaimer: All the characters in this story are fictitious and any resemblence to any person living or deceased is purely coincidental

.

Contents

	Introduction	1
PART I	**THE TIME IS NOW**	
Chapter 1:	Time to Go	7
2:	Enter Harley	13
3:	EGO as Guide	21
4:	Dying Into It	27
5:	Higher Self As Guide	35
6:	Spiritual Amnesia	39
7:	The Big Bang	43
8:	Personal Soul Growth	49
9:	Choosing Parents	53
PART II	**INCARNATION SCHOOL**	
10:	Pain in the Bank	63
11:	America's Bank Account	71
12:	Past Life Carry-Over	81
13:	Perception is Everything	85
14:	America's Shadow Stuff	89
PART III	**THE MISSION**	
15:	Mission Revealed	97
16:	America's Soul Destiny	105
17	Prophecies	109
18:	Enter Sadeem	115
19:	My Parents	121
20:	The Plan Unfolds	127
21:	Showdown	135
22:	Mirrors	141

23:	Hot Buttons	147
24:	Break-down	157
25:	Break-through	163
26:	Ready to Go	169
PART IV	**DOWN TO EARTH**	
27:	The In-body Experience	177
28:	Fantasy vs. Science	185
29:	The Bridge to Peace	199
Appendix I	Assumptions of Radical Forgiveness	213
	The Evolution of Consciousness	220

ACKNOWLEDGMENTS

There are many wonderful people who have contributed to this book simply by being in my life. To name a few would be to exclude far too many who would deserve mention, so I am simply going thank my wife, JoAnna, for her love and support and leave it at that. To everyone else who would be mentioned if I had several pages on which to do it — and you know who you are — I send my love and gratitude.

Introduction

Have you ever wondered why you are here, or perhaps found yourself wondering whether you came into this life with some sort of a "mission?" If so, then you are not alone. Many people seem to experience a longing to find something that will give their lives meaning beyond mere existence.

Assume for a moment that it is true that we do indeed all come into the life experience with a pre-planned purpose or mission. Do you have a sense of what that might be for you? Is your purpose connected with your God-given talent for example, or with the work that you do? Were you *called* to do something with your life? When you look back, do you sense that everything that has happened to you only makes sense in terms of it leading to the purpose for which you were born?

What if you were born to do something really big - something that was way beyond that which you do in life, or how you personally express your talent? What if this mission has not been revealed to you yet? What incredibly fabulous story are you possibly weaving with the circumstances of your life that will suddenly reveal itself as the outplaying of a mission pre-ordained and meticulously carried out?

In my book, *'Radical Forgiveness, Making Room for the Miracle,'* I suggest that Princess Diana's sudden death was meaningful in terms of her spiritual mission to open the heart chakra of England. Everything that happened, including the tragic death itself, was seen as entirely purposeful in creating the highly charged context necessary for her mission to be achieved. It could be said that her whole life had meaning only in terms of that mission. It can therefore be said that her mission was a total success and to that extent, hers was indeed ***a radical incarnation.***

However Princess Di's mission pales in comparison to that of Jack Barber whom you will not meet in human form until close to the end of the book. You will however, soon come to know him well as a soul who is being carefully prepared and tutored for his soul journey into humanity and his mission, by Harley, his Angel of Incarnation. You will accompany him through all his tutorials with Harley and be witness to his anxiety as the enormity of his mission dawns upon him.

Jack starts out thinking that he is very much a humble soul who will, like most souls, be given a quite ordinary mission but later begins to realize, as the story unfolds, that he is being prepared for something very big indeed - something vitally important to the contemporary world. In this sense Jack's mission will affect every one of us and it will involve us all.

Jack is destined to become someone we all know extremely well and we will get to see Jack's mission played out in front of our eyes - on the world stage.

Jack is already incarnate so the drama that will provide the context in which the mission will happen, has already begun. On the surface, his life is proceeding ordinarily on the Earth Plane just like every other soul on its human journey.

Even though as yet, he has no awareness of his mission, everything is coming together according to plan. The major players in the drama are in total readiness and all the stages are being arranged as you read. Much of the work in setting the scenes has been accomplished.

Through this book you actually become privy to what this mission is - even in advance of Jack *(as a human being)* knowing it. In fact, the readers of this book are the only ones who have the awareness that Jack's mission might change the world completely and shift mass consciousness in such a way that as to create two thousand years of peace, harmony and bliss. Conversely, you also know the price we shall all pay if the mission fails. The stakes could not be higher.

Though we know what the mission is, we have no idea at this time how it will actually occur. All we can do is wait and see how it unfolds and to the extent that it might involve each and every one of us, participate in the drama as fully as possible.

We should do this in the knowledge that something wonderful is about to happen, in spite of how it looks now. When it does, we will be the first to recognize it as the greatest breakthrough in consciousness in all of human history. It is no exaggeration to say, therefore, that what you have in your hands right now is the greatest thriller ever written, and you are in it!

Yes, you! You and me both, in fact — plus a few hundred thousand other souls who are being called upon to raise their vibration, shift their consciousness and create Heaven on Earth in our time. You see — Jack's mission turns out to be our mission too! We're all in this together.

Are you ready?

You have the power to change the world, create genuine world peace and bring about a spiritual awakening.

It's easier than you could possibly imagine!

Willing?

READ ON

and

ENJOY

PART ONE

The Time is 'NOW'

1: Time to Go

The message came down at 4:21.04. My application had been accepted. I was to show up at the very next Incarnation Orientation meeting at 10:30.00 to receive my instructions. Oh, what bliss! At last I would have the opportunity to be human — something I had been waiting for, seemingly for eons. So many times had I applied to go and so often had I been told that I was not well enough evolved to undertake a human assignment. Now it seemed that all my spiritual study and hard work had paid off.

I decided then that I would ask that I be born into the human experience at precisely 3:42.20 for no other reason than that the numbers added up to be my soul identity number.

You might have noticed how precise I have become with this particularly human thought form called time. My angelic tutors had been really prepping me on this, in the expectation that I would be soon doing my earth walk, and had actually given me a thought form called a 'Rolex watch.' This is a thought form that, once in physical form, is for some reason especially valued on the earth plane, so I was honored to receive it.

My willingness to master this particularly strange form of existential awareness, even before being accepted in the program, may have tipped the scales in my favor. I had become very adept at demonstrating how the 'now' can be stretched backwards and forwards into what they on the earth plane call 'past' and 'future.' They divide time into very small increments called years, months, days, hours, minutes and seconds and to them it seems quite real. They seem to take it quite seriously anyway.

I found I could have a lot of fun with it myself and impress other souls with how well I could actually tell what time it was. Even the angels would come to me, laughing and giggling, saying, *"Hey Jack, what time is it now?"* Everyone thought it rather silly, but it didn't matter. I knew it would come in handy in the 'nows' to come, even if it was totally irrelevant in this world.

I thought myself to the Incarnation Orientation meeting at the appointed 'now.' *(By my Rolex watch thought form, I knew it was exactly 10:30. I hadn't mastered the am/pm distinction yet, nor even the meaning of early or late, but that didn't matter. I just thought it was cool being able to put a number to the particular 'now' that we were experiencing. Those finer distinctions I would have to learn on the job so to speak).*

A lot of other souls were there too, many of whom I recognized. These were going to be the members of my soul group,

I surmised—rightly as it turned out. Later I would learn that some would be doing their Earth-walk at the same time as I myself, while others would not incarnate at all but remain here at 'mission control' pulling the strings, so to speak.

To my surprise, I was also to learn that for every one soul incarnating there would be seven souls remaining on this side. No wonder there were so many souls in the room.

I suddenly learned what it might feel like to experience panic. Suppose I was to be one of the team of seven and not, after all, the one to incarnate? I knew that each was as important as the other and that I shouldn't really be attached to anything one way or another, but in all honesty I had rather set my heart on incarnating into the human experience myself.

What I didn't realize at the time, but was to see clearly upon my return home, was that I was already starting to take on human egoistic tendencies even at this stage. I was finding myself wanting, expecting and being attached to particular outcomes. I was noticing too that I was setting myself up for disappointment if my expectations weren't met; seeing one way of being as 'better than;' and most of all, being already fascinated by, if not completely attached to, the illusionary notion of time.

I was also going to be shown on my return home that my purpose for incarnation was precisely to transform these latent tendencies that lay within me. But there was much that would happen in between.

An air of great expectancy filled the space. The room itself being circular, the seating was arranged in a circle so that all those seated could focus their LOVE on the beings standing on the circular platform of light at the center. Angels stood all around the periphery, singing softly in adoration and praise.

In a moment, one of the beings raised up and began calling out the names of those that would form each of the groups of eight souls. Once this was completed we instantly came together in our groups. To my surprise *(and consternation given my desire to be the 'one')*, it became apparent that we were to vote on which soul out of the eight was to incarnate. Our task was to match the best candidate for the mission that the elders had assigned to our soul group. The elders had apparently chosen each group on the basis of being the best team to work on a particular mission, but were leaving it to the group to decide on the 'one.'

There being no secrets in this world each soul in the group knew the strengths and weaknesses in each other so each of us pleaded for the others on the basis of who would best be able to fulfill the mission that the elders had given us.

I was glad to hear that each of them wanted to be the 'one' as much as I. Paradoxically, once I knew this I surrendered completely and became totally committed to having it be the most perfect soul for the job. As it turned out, I was the one selected.

Once this was decided the next task was to come together with our incarnation angel to discuss the mission, or to be more precise, missions. I stress the plural because of a recent edict that had come down from above to the effect that souls would take on a lot more than they had in previous times. Consciousness on planet Earth had shifted dramatically since the Harmonic Convergence (1987) which meant that incarnating souls were now able to take on many more assignments than before.

2: Enter Harley

Our Angel of Incarnation was called Harley. He was an extremely old soul with great wisdom and a deep capacity to LOVE. He had sent many of the great souls to Earth, many of whom had had tremendous impact on that plane. Galileo, Plato, Martin Buber, Bagwan Shree Ragneesh and Martin Luther King were among them. degree of suffering was necessary for humans to endure in order to help them awaken.

Harley congratulated me on being elected as the one to incarnate. At the same time he pointed out that I had the hardest job out of the seven souls.

"It will look quite easy from up here," he said. "But once you get down there where the energy is really dense and heavy, it will seem very different. You will feel really heavy and at times you will feel like you are trying to swim through molasses. Life will seem like a huge struggle.

"The other seven souls will be up here in total support of you, of course, but you must understand that they won't really be able to appreciate how hard it will be for you. They might be tempted to pile too much onto you, not really knowing how problematic that might be for you in human terms.

"This means that you have to be clear in your requests to them. Ask for what you want in very clear terms – and if they become too demanding and overly creative, tell them to back off for a while. They will not understand the effect that their assignments might have on your human body, so you must stay aware of that yourself. We'll maybe intervene with some occasional psychic surgery if you ask for it, but by and large we expect you to be in charge of everything pertaining to your physical health and well-being."

In spite of everything Harley had said about how difficult this might be, I still felt really good about being the 'one.' I had after all been preparing for it and had always known I would do an Earth-walk at some 'now.'

Harley then went on to explain that I would have a number of missions, some major and some minor and that there would be some specific lessons for me to learn.

At one point he gave me a long hard and penetrating stare. It was then that I realized that he had something pretty important for me to do and that my main mission would not be inconsequential. Although normal practice was to let everyone know the mission early on, he obviously wasn't yet ready to divulge what it was in my case. That was unnerving to say the least. After the long stare he shifted gears and began to describe the nature of the journey.

"In order for your soul to incarnate as an apparently separate individual, it will have to go through a metamorphosis so you can enter the portal that will take you into the world of Humanity. This process has already begun, though you might not have noticed anything yet.

"Whereas here in this world your soul is limitless, when you enter the World of Humanity as an energy pattern vibrating at the frequency of potential physicality, it will become more bounded in the space/time continuum. As you go though the portal it will have to squeeze itself into a much smaller, human version of a soul with several different aspects. Some of these will continue to change all throughout your human life while others will remain pretty constant.

"For instance, you will be assigned a basic character. Much of that will come from the genes of your parents, which is one reason why we have to choose those people carefully. Your character will change hardly at all throughout your whole life. On the other hand, that which we refer to as your personality, which we also have a hand in designing up here before you go in, will be much more flexible and subject to some modification in response to the events that you co-create throughout your life.

"Many of the factors that will make up your character and aspects of your personality, and of course your exact date of birth, will be determined up here by reference to the sacred numbers of numerology and all relevant astrological considerations, especially as they relate to where you should be born, to whom, in what age-time and for what purpose.

"Once established, this will form the basic blueprint for your life. However, don't imagine that everything is set up in advance and that life is just a matter of fate. Or that we up here are controlling or micro-managing what you do down there.

"No, you are given complete free will to create your life as you see fit in the moment. You will be continually referencing your blueprint and acting from there but exactly how you will do it will definitely be up to you. Deep down you will know your purpose for being in a human body, but exactly how you will express it, (or choose not to express it, for that is an option, too), will again be up to you. You will know what lessons you have come in to learn but how you will create them is definitely for you to decide."

Being somewhat puzzled about this, I had to ask, "But Harley, what about the Divine Plan? Doesn't the term plan mean that it is something fixed and unalterable? How can it be a plan if every aspect of it is subject to change by each individual soul? That sounds like a recipe for chaos to me."

"Yes, there is the Divine Plan," Harley replied, " but it is continually unfolding in every moment and you are part of that unfoldment, moment by moment. Every action taken by every soul on the planet in every moment changes the Divine Plan for the next moment. Yet nothing gets out of balance. It is always in perfect alignment with what is called for at that moment.

"Think of it as a very intricate design or pattern on a computer screen, beautifully arranged to be in perfect balance all the time. As each tiny element of the overall pattern is altered, the computer program kicks in and rearranges all the other elements to fit the new arrangement so as to maintain the balance. It is so wonderfully intelligent in this regard that when all is said and done, nothing matters. It all gets worked out in that moment. Everything is always perfect and at every moment expressing the consciousness of God, which of course is LOVE.

"That, in essence, is the Divine Plan. LOVE is all there is and your part in this is simply to know yourself as LOVE."

"That's easy," I interrupted. "I already am LOVE."

"It's only easy when you are up here," he replied. "Yes, of course you know that you are LOVE. But the challenge for you when you become human is that, for at least quite a large chunk of your life, you will not know this at all. All that you know about yourself as a spiritual being will be hidden — buried deep down in the unconscious part of your mind. You will not know who you are.

"However, the objective of the whole exercise is to discover it, to remember yourself and the truth of who you really are. At that point you will be able to fully experience yourself as LOVE in a way that is not possible up here.

"You see Jack, up here we can only *know* that we are LOVE. Down there, because we have a body with which to feel it, we can really *experience* ourselves as LOVE. The feeling experience is one of pure bliss.

"That's the fun part of the whole human experience. When, after experiencing the apparent difficulties inherent in living on the Earth plane, you begin to awaken to the fact that it is all really just an illusion and a trick of the mind and that LOVE ***is*** all there is, it will become for you a huge cosmic joke. You will have what is known down there as a 'breakthrough' or a 'realization' or a 'transformative experience.' You won't be able to stop smiling."

"But what if I don't awaken to this truth?" I asked. "What happens then? And how will I know to awaken at all if I am unconscious?"

"Many don't awaken," replied Harley. "And that's OK. They are still in service to others by co-creating all sorts of situations which, while they stay asleep, enable their co-creators to awaken to the truth. Remember everything is perfect. They will awaken when the time is right. If you have to live your whole life asleep in order to serve the greater good, that's how it is meant to be. Don't be attached to awakening."

"Oh, but I will want to awaken, Harley!" I interjected. "The last thing I want to do is to go down there and spend all my time concerned exclusively with earthly matters, only to find when I get back here, that I didn't connect with the truth of who I am. I will have wasted the opportunity. And what about my soul group here? They would be very disappointed. I would feel that I had let them down."

"One of the things I have been noticing about you Jack, as you have progressed up the spiritual ladder of knowledge is that you are not yet free of attachment to particular outcomes.

You still have a need to control things and you continually set yourself up for disappointment, even at this level of your development. That's why we are strongly suggesting that you set up lessons for yourself during your forthcoming human life that will teach you about these things. We will talk more about this later, though.

"In any case, Jack, it is not a requirement that everyone has to awaken together in order to raise the consciousness of all. The critical mass required to shift everyone into the fourth and fifth dimension is actually quite small relative to the entire number of souls on the planet at any one time. It will only require a certain number of people to remember for critical mass to occur. When that is reached, everyone will shift. But until that happens, the few who will struggle to create that critical mass will need a whole lot of souls to push against to make the process viable. If you happen to be one of those, Jack, you will have served God just as mightily as if you had been a shining beacon of wakefulness. Remember, the world of Humanity is a world of duality. Those who will break through need to feel the resistance of the many who are afraid. It's all part of the plan. You will do what you are led to do, Jack, so stop worrying."

I felt the sting of Harley's comments about my addiction to attachment to outcome. He was right of course. I have always had difficulty in surrendering. It clearly has been my main lesson all the way through. I was feeling some trepidation now because I knew by what Harley had already said that I was going to experience some pretty strong lessons in surrendering while I was on the Earth Plane. I just hoped I would be able to recognize them as lessons early enough in life to be able to move through them. But then, here I go again, trying to anticipate and being attached to that outcome. Gee, this surrender thing is really difficult, even up here. Imagine how hard it will be down there!

"Let me address the point of how you will know to awaken," Harley continued. "Here's where you will get some help. Besides your soul team up here, you will have a couple of guides along with you, sitting on your shoulder all the way through, guiding you towards that point of knowing whether or not to awaken. Both of them are aspects of your own soul, but in the process of your shrinking yourself down so as to fit the human version of the soul, they will become differentiated. They will certainly feel separate from you even while carrying on a conversation with you from within. The first is the one known as your Ego. The second is your Higher Self."

3: Ego As Guide

Harley continued. "I will speak first about the Ego," he said. "It is probably the most fascinating of the two and certainly the least understood part of who you will become while in a human body.

"This aspect of yourself will be very instrumental in creating all of the many circumstances of your life that will constitute your learning opportunities. We will have very little control over your Ego from up here, except inasmuch as we have had to preprogram it to some extent to take you in certain predetermined directions consistent with your mission. But don't worry, your Ego is very creative and has a tremendous sense of humor. Combine this with a predilection for irony and taste for the absurd, this guide is going to take you where you need to go even if you have to go kicking and screaming!

"Its main role of course is to completely sell you on the idea that you are separate not only from every other human and animal species, but from the Earth itself and ultimately, God.

This guide will sell you on that long held and totally ridiculous idea that man made a decision to separate from God and that was his undoing. It will persuade you that this caused God to get very angry."

I opened my mouth to protest, but Harley was ready for me. He put up his hand and said, "I know, I know! You're thinking how can a God that is all-loving be angry, and how can you separate from that which you are yourself?

"Well, I've already warned you that things do get quite bizarre down there, especially where God is concerned. There are more myths about God than you can shake a stick at, and groups get to kill millions of people defending some of these ridiculous ideas. But that's humanity. Don't you just love 'em?" joked Harley.

"I'm not sure as I can right now," I answered. "Especially as I am about to become one of them. Will I get to be so self-righteous about my idea of Universal Intelligence that I would kill someone in defense of my ideas?"

"Quite likely, Jack. In any case, there are lots of ways to kill people without actually killing them, you know. You can kill with words even. People seem to be very willing to be cruel to each other in defense of their righteousness about almost anything.

"Anyway, as I was saying," Harley continued, "the Ego will say that not only is God extremely angry that his children have separated (fallen), but is also hell bent on punishing them very severely once he catches up with them.

"It is through this story that the Ego teaches you fear and guilt. Fear that you have incurred the wrath of God, and stand a good chance of being sent to Hell forever, and guilt for having committed that 'original sin.'

"In turn, in order to protect yourself from the fear and the guilt, the Ego teaches you how to repress those feelings and then, in order to get rid of them, to project them onto other people. This sets up a wonderful matrix of relationships between people who are not only in denial about themselves but are continually projecting onto others and being projected upon. This obviously becomes fertile ground for the creation of many different kinds of learning opportunities. What a genius this Ego is!"

"Harley, what is repression and projection?" I enquired. "I'm not sure I understood that last bit. Can you explain?"

"It would take too long Jack," said Harley quickly. "In any case you will be receiving some very specific classes very soon on those aspects of human behavior, so I don't need to go into them right now. But I can tell you this. You are going to get to play with repression and projection big time in your incarnation." Then once more he gave me that long penetrating stare that was so unnerving to me.

"Anyway, let's get back to the Ego. To get things well prepared before all that kind of fun starts, your Ego will help you develop into a fully differentiated autonomous being, with a strong sense of self, but with virtually no awareness of your connection with the All That Is.

"This is purposeful for it is not until you reach this stage where separation seems so self evident and irrefutable that your lessons can begin. The Ego does one hell of a good job in achieving this in almost everyone.

"The Ego is also the specialist in helping you to become fully immersed in, and committed to, believing in all the illusions of the physical world. By that I mean, not only separation, but duality, right and wrong, good and bad, pain and suffering and of course, death. Giving you a strong fear of death and the concomitant idea of total annihilation through death is the Ego's master stroke."

"Why would that be?" I asked.

"Well, if everyone knew that death was simply an illusion and that there was absolutely nothing in it to fear, people would keep choosing it just to escape the discomfort of the human existence. That would undermine the whole enterprise–which is what, Jack? Let's see if you have it."

"It's to take on a body and be immersed in a world of separation and the opposite of LOVE so that I can go beyond just knowing that I am LOVE to the full experience of it–emotionally and physically as well as intellectually," I answered with as much confidence as I could muster. I realized as I heard myself say it, that I was mouthing off a pat answer, betraying a shallow understanding of the idea.

"And just how and when will you have that experience, Jack? How, when you are in that world of conditionality, duality, change and separation, are you going to experience the real truth of who you are?"

Harley had me in a corner and I was very uncomfortable. I couldn't find an answer to his question.

"Since unconditional LOVE is impossible down there, under what circumstances can you see yourself experiencing full unconditional LOVE to the point where you actually become that?" Harley paused–presumably to give me time to think.

"See the problem, Jack?"

"Yes, I do," I replied thoughtfully. "It makes you wonder why we even go there at all. If we want to experience ourselves as LOVE why go to a place where so little of it exists? To become truly loving in the World of Humanity, one would have to overcome incredible resistance, wouldn't we?"

"That's exactly the point, Jack!" said Harley, leaping high into the air. "To fully become LOVE you have to transcend everything that appears not to be LOVE. The human experience will throw at you everything that is not LOVE in order to test you.

"There is nowhere more suitable in the Universe for this kind of schooling. If you really want to move to the next level of spiritual development, Jack, this is what you need. This kind of environment will give you the context for all the lessons that you need to learn, not only for yourself but all other souls–and ultimately God."

That last comment startled me. "What do you mean 'ultimately God? Did I understand you to mean that I am incarnating for God's benefit? Harley, I need you to explain that!"

"Not now, Jack. It will take a little time to explain how when we incarnate we are each contributing to the expansion of the mind of Universal Intelligence. I did not mean to startle you and I'm sorry I dropped it on you without the necessary preparation. We'll definitely come back to it."

With that, Harley disappeared.

4: Dying Into It

As soon Harley reappeared, the conversation continued as if nothing had happened. "Now, where were we before I got us off track?" said Harley.

"You were saying how perfect the World of Humanity is for providing us with precisely the experiences we need for our spiritual development," I reminded him.

"That's right. Think of the human experience as a spiritual boot camp—the best that ever existed. Like all boot camps it is designed to build you up by tearing you down until you surrender completely. Your Ego is the equivalent of your personal Sergeant Major, drilling you day after day until you begin to perform exactly according to the rules of being human. Your Ego will tell you what to think, what to do, where to go, what to believe, who to hang out with, what to judge, how to lay blame, how to cheat and betray others, how to compete and win at all costs, hoard money, lust after power, etc. In short, how to become a fully differentiated, individual human being concerned only with his own survival. Perfect!

"However, the World of Humanity differs from a boot camp in one important but crucial degree. People who go to boot camp always have a very clear training goal in mind. Motivation is very high because everyone wants to graduate with honors. The 'School of Humanity' boot camp, by contrast, has no recognizable goal. No one seems to know why they are there; neither do they have the vaguest notion of what the whole thing is about, or when it might end. Such a situation does not, as I am sure you will agree, have a shred of intrinsic motivation attached to it."

"So what keeps people in the program?" I had to ask. "If it's as unpleasant as it sounds and there appears to be no reason to be doing it, why do people make such a strong point of doing it for as long as they can?"

"Simple," replied Harley. "The fear of death. The fear of ceasing to exist. That's what keeps them in the program. You have to hand it to the Ego, Jack. First it seduces you into believing that you are a separate entity, existing alone — separate from other human beings and separate from the source of infinite supply and security — God, and to all intent and purposes, independent and self-reliant. Then it teaches you to fear death — which we up here know to be the way back home — to such a degree that you hang on to life at all costs and never give up trying to keep death away. While it is true that the pain of being separate and alone may be almost unbearable, it is still preferable to the only alternative — death. Fear of death, Jack. That's the motivation. Perfect, don't you think?"

"I guess it is," I agreed. "But is that the only purpose of making death fearful — to create a kind of prison without bars from which no-one wants to escape? Sounds like that idea of keeping an elephant chained to a stump until he gets so used to it that, even when the chain is removed, it doesn't move away from the mooring because it doesn't know that it is free."

"Yes, it is similar in that one sense. But there is more to it than that, Jack. The fear of death raises the bar for achieving a meaningful level of transcendence through the actual death process. If there was little fear there would be little challenge to it. The journey of life is nothing more than a march towards death and the purpose of life, my friend, is to face our worst fear and transcend it."

"How do we transcend it?" I enquired.

"By surrendering."

"Surrendering to what, though?"

"You'll find out, Jack. Until you know what it feels like to be in a human body facing death, you can't imagine how it is. You will have spent the whole of your life thinking that you are sufficient unto yourself and in control of your destiny. As you slide towards death you realize that you are powerless to control anything and that you are moving into the void, into nothingness, into non-existence. There's nothing more terrifying for human beings than the idea that they don't exist. And that's what death represents to them.

"We have set it up in precisely that way so that when they transcend their fear of death and go through the experience and discover that "not existing" means becoming once again ONE with God, their awareness of what that means will be magnified many hundreds of times. Can you see how that would raise the transcendence bar, Jack?"

"Yes, I think so," I replied thoughtfully. "It gives spiritual value to the whole experience. The higher the bar is set, the greater my growth through the process of transcendence. And in the moment that I find myself back home in this world, I will realize that my fear of death was in direct proportion to the bliss that I am feeling on this side."

"That's right," said Harley. "Now you're starting to get it. ***It is not death that is the doorway to the sublime; it's the fear of death.*** The sublime arises in the realization that not only is death an illusion but so is separation. Cool, isn't it?"

"I guess so," I replied.

"Up here, we have known this forever, of course. We know that separation is not the truth and just take it for granted that we souls exist in the same relationship to the Whole as a wave is in relation to the ocean. We think of Universal Intelligence as being a vast ocean of consciousness. Each one of us souls arises from that ocean and then at the right and perfect moment, falls back into it to become the ocean again.

"For us then, death is nothing—just part of the song of existence. Since we know that we are existence itself, ceasing to exist is nothing to us, anymore than it would be for a wave.

"But when you're human, you don't know that. Humans can't conceive of themselves just dying into the ocean of consciousness. Not only do they avoid death at all costs during their life, but they try to buy comfort for themselves by making up stories about how they might continue to exist as themselves even after death. They imagine themselves basically continuing life "up there" more or less as they have known it "down here.

"Of course, there is truth in that but if only it were that simple!" said Harley, rolling his eyes and shaking his head from side to side as if going over in his mind how it really is in this World of Spirit as opposed to how human beings make it up.

"They also try to ensure their immortality," he continued, "by imagining that they will come back again in a new lifetime as themselves, not realizing of course that once you have fallen back into the great sea of consciousness — into the ONENESS, you will never arise again as the same being—just as the wave that falls back into the ocean will never be that same wave again. In the same way that the ocean is constantly changing its form, God is continually recreating itself anew in every moment.

"Transcending death in order to magnify our awareness of the LOVE vibration and ONENESS, is the great quest that each of us takes when we go down to the Earth Plane. Deep down human beings know this. You can tell that they do by reading their mythology."

"Do you have an example of that?" I asked.

"Yes, there's one about a knight slaying the dragon. In order to win the LOVE of the princess (goddess), the knight, having undergone years of training realizes that he has now to find the courage to search out and enter into mortal combat with the dragon (the Ego), fully prepared to die (transcend) in the process if necessary. Once the dragon is slain (died to the Ego), the knight can then claim the princess as his bride and know LOVE (Oneness)."

"Is this true for every soul, Harley?," I asked. "Do they all make it home to find joy and bliss?"

"Eventually they all do," replied Harley, "but some don't go straight there. Their bodies die but the fear of death may have been magnified to such an extent that they are too terrified to go to the light. Their religion may have taught them that they have sinned badly and that God is going to punish them very severely when they die. Some religions teach them that they will be sent to a place called Hell where they will burn in perpetuity. Crazy idea, I know, but that's the kind of thing they do down there.

"And it's a very different form of fear than the 'existential angst' that we have been talking about and have set up for them. No, that's really dark energy and we don't like to create that since it is totally counterproductive. Why turn them away from the very experience that life has set up for them—the experience of LOVE and Bliss through transcendence?"

"So what happens to them," I asked, silently hoping I wouldn't have a religion that would do that to me. It doesn't matter that Hell doesn't exist, but I'm sure the fear of it is almost as bad. I wouldn't want to be stuck in that energy."

"Well, as you can imagine, the idea of going towards that light is anathema to them. Why would they go there if they are that certain that they are going to be sent to Hell? So rather than do that, they choose to hang out in the Astral plane for a while, which is a kind of spiritual Never-Never Land. Some even try to get back to the Earth plane by renting space in someone else's body. Actually renting may not be the right word–squatting would be a more accurate description since the host doesn't even know he or she has company.

"These lost souls hang around hospitals a lot because when people are under anesthesia it is very easy for a soul to jump in and occupy space. Same is true of bars because when people are drunk or on drugs a soul can slip in quite easily."

"So how long do they stay lost in Never-Never Land?" I asked.

"Hard to tell, and anyway that question is irrelevant because there is no time. Nevertheless, the way it works is that eventually an angel comes along and persuades them that their fear is ungrounded; there is no Hell, God doesn't punish anyone and that LOVE awaits them if they would simply move towards it."

"So everyone makes it in the end?" I wanted to absolutely make sure of this point. I didn't fancy the idea of being some kind of ghost stuck in the Astral plane.

"Yes, but there is another group that experiences difficulty in making it, at least initially. These are those who die without the opportunity to contemplate their death because they die very suddenly, perhaps under cataclysmic circumstances.

"They will often find themselves in the Astral plane for a while, purely out of confusion. It takes them a while to know that they are even dead. But we have a team of Angels always standing by to bring them home, so they make it too, eventually. They don't remain stuck for long, not like the others.

"OK, that's enough about the Ego and all that it creates for you in your human experience. Let's take a break."

Harley vanished.

5: The Higher Self As Guide

Harley reappeared and uncharacteristically took a seat. He had remained standing all the while prior to this session.

"I want to talk now about your other guide — the Higher Self. Just like the Ego, it will come into being the moment you squeeze through that portal and emerge into the World of Humanity.

"Now, of course, in that world there is an alchemy of opposites so it is perfectly in alignment with your reality now that there should be two guides who appear to be opposites.

"They will tend to always pull you in different directions. The Ego will pull you away from ONENESS while the Higher Self will always want to be reminding you of the truth of who you are. But that's their job. That's exactly what they are supposed to do for you.

"The Ego and the Higher Self are not therefore in competition with each other. Neither are they in mortal combat as some spiritual philosophies suggest. Even though it will seem as though the Ego will be calling all the shots, believe me, your Higher Self is in total cahoots with the Ego. They confer all the time and together set things up for you to experience.

"However, the Higher Self is the softer of the two and for the most part is there to balance things out a bit. It will help you discover a bunch of spiritual practices that will keep you connected, albeit by a very fine thread, to the World of Spirit. These are things like Radical Forgiveness,* prayer, meditation, contemplation and many forms of spiritual healing.

"These 'antidotes' will help you get through your difficulties without taking away their value. In fact, when the antidotes are added into the mix the benefit of having the difficulties to work through is magnified many times and everything is speeded up enormously. That means much more can be accomplished. You learn more about this in a later lesson.

"From time to time the Higher Self will lift the veil a little–just for a moment or two–to give you a glimpse of spiritual reality. There might be a number of reasons for this, but basically the Higher Self will do it to jump start a dramatic shift in your awareness. However, this is the exception rather than the rule. For the most part, the Higher Self will simply lead you in that

* By the time you have finished this book you will know exactly what constitutes Radical Forgiveness for, in truth, that is what this book is all about. However, in Appendix I, you will find the underlying assumptions and principles of Radical Forgiveness spelled out.

direction giving you all manner of hints along the way. These hints will come in the form of synchronicities, signs, tarot card readings, dreams, flash insights, automatic writing experiences like the one that our brother and teacher soul Neale Donald Walsch has demonstrated to the whole world, to name but a few.

"But there are many ways in which the Higher Self will attempt to remind us of the truth and of course, you will find the physical world itself and what humans call 'nature' to be a great source for spiritual inspiration.

"But here's what you have to understand, Jack. We have set it up so that Human Beings can only experience that reality in a very limited way. We have given them five senses that can only work over a very limited frequency range, perceiving only physical realities.

"Viewed through these senses, the physical world looks so real that you can quite understand why human beings would believe that it is real and that there is nothing else. We have done a good job in that regard, but on the other hand it has made the Higher Self's job quite difficult. It has all but cut people off from hearing its message at all, no matter how many subtle messages the Higher Self has tried to give.

"Fortunately, humans are now becoming more sensitive to the Higher Self and are becoming more open to the idea that their Higher Self is communicating all the time and giving them guidance. That is making things a whole lot easier and is speeding up the entire process which, as we shall see later, is crucial.

"In the first three or four years of life you will be intimately connected to your Higher Self and in those tender years may even be able to remember being here in this World of Spirit. As a young child you exist quite comfortably in both worlds at the same time.

"But then, as the awareness of this world fades from your consciousness and the veil thickens, the Ego will begin to dominate. Your Higher Self will be in the background observing and guiding where necessary, but it will mostly stay out of the Ego's way during the time that you are learning how to be completely separated and self contained. Once this has occurred, you will begin to become aware of the voice of the Higher Self within you gently whispering to you ideas of ONENESS, unconditional LOVE, harmony and peace."

"Sounds like a whole lot of fun," I said looking around at my soul team. "Being briefed to this extent should make it a piece of cake."

I was soon to learn the error of what I had just said.

6: Spiritual Amnesia

Jumping up out of the chair he had only just allowed him self, he exclaimed as if completely taken aback by my comment. "Oh, didn't I tell you? Once you go through the portal you won't remember a thing about this world, nor any of what I am telling you, nor what you are about to learn in your classes.

"Spiritual amnesia is an absolute necessity, Jack. If you knew that every one of your experiences were simply setups, you wouldn't participate at the required emotional level. You would simply opt out of every one of them. The whole idea is to experience human existence as fully as possible and to go through it in the belief that it is real so that when you come back here your awareness of ONENESS is magnified many hundreds of times. Without total amnesia this magnification would never occur."

I was in total shock at this point, so much so that I left for a few moments and went wizzing about the Universe in a frenzy of frenetic energy. I collected myself and returned to the 'now.'

I felt very silly. I had been under the impression that Harley was telling me all this so I would have an advantage. I didn't realize that every soul that incarnated was given the very same classes that I was getting. Foolishly, I thought I was getting special treatment. *(I guess wanting to be special is a human thing – another indication that my vibration was moving in that direction already).* Nevertheless it was a shock to learn that I would remember nothing of this reality – and scary too. Harley had spoken earlier about how the end of life is a process of moving into the void through the process of dying, but it seems it's just the same at this end.

Pulling myself together quickly and feeling defensive and not a little angry, I shot back at Harley, "Then why are you telling me all this, and why do I have to attend all these lessons if I am to forget everything? That makes no sense at all!"

Harley picked up that I was already having human emotions and that I had had expectations about being given special treatment and was on the defensive. He became gentle and kind in his response.

"Every soul in this world is special, Jack, each in their own way. You are very special and you are valued for who you are and the gifts that you bring to this world. But no one gets special treatment, Jack. That would be to create separation. I know that you are only feeling that now because your vibration is beginning to get low enough for you to connect with human emotions, so don't make yourself wrong for it. That's exactly what needs to happen."

I felt better immediately. What a loving, kindly soul Harley was. He was such a great teacher and I knew that the lessons I was about to have would be wonderful experiences. "Thanks Harley," I said, quietly.

"No problem, Jack," he acknowledged, softly. "Now, let me return to your question about why we are giving you all this information if you won't remember it. Well, for one thing it will program your Ego and Higher Self so they will know exactly what to do when you are on the Earth Plane. You, of course, won't remember anything but those two will act with total awareness. Your education will come into play as you begin to gradually remember who you are. When your Higher Self begins to whisper to you, you will draw on these lessons from way down in your unconscious mind. Everything that I am telling you now will be down there but you will have no awareness of it – at least until your Higher Self decides that the time is right to enlighten you about it."

That was reassuring at least. His assurances that I wasn't going down there with absolutely no lifeline, nor without a couple of guides who knew what the heck they were doing, made me feel a lot better. I guess the only thing to do was to trust the process.

"Let's take another break," said Harley, vanishing immediately.

7: The Big Bang

Upon Harley's return we continued the discussion—or rather the monologue because I wasn't saying enough to warrant my calling it a discussion. Harley picked up exactly where he had left off.

"Earlier in our discourse I sidetracked the issue of all this being purposeful in terms of the need that Universal Intelligence has to continue expanding its consciousness. Let's deal with it now because it is central to everything.

"Jack, do you have any idea how Universal Intelligence and everything else came into being?"

"Not really," I said, looking at all the others to make sure I was not the only one in ignorance of something so vitally important. "But I would like to know. I've never questioned it before. I have always taken it for granted that Universal Intelligence had always existed."

"Well, not exactly," said Harley. "Let me try to explain it to you as simply as I can. It is not easy to comprehend, so pay attention.

"You've heard of the Big Bang theory, haven't you? Humans have spent a long time developing this theory and to tell you the truth, they are not far off the mark. The only bit they haven't yet fully understood is of course the most important part of the whole thing. And that is the bit about what was prior to the big bang. Because they are so locked into the idea of time and space, they can't imagine anything coming into being without there being something before. It's a real problem for them.

"The truth is though that there was nothing before the big bang. Except consciousness – pure potential that's all. That is until consciousness gave birth to the very first thought."

"What was that?" I asked nervously and with great expectancy.

"What if there is something else?" Harley replied dramatically.

"That's it?"

"That was it," said Harley. "In the very instant that this thought occurred within that field of consciousness, the Big Bang occurred. The material universe manifested immediately in that very moment and in that instant Universal Consciousness became intelligent. **God was**."

Harley stood there looking triumphant as if he himself had been solely responsible for the Big Bang. We all stood there speechless, but he was so excited he hardly drew breath before going on.

"As you know from your previous studies, the material universe has continued to grow and expand. Scientists have actually measured the rate at which it is expanding. However, just as the material universe has continued to grow and expand so has Universal Intelligence. God needs to continue expanding its consciousness in exactly the same way, for it too is part of that same expanding universe. You will notice that even on earth people talk about God as 'the Universe.' This is no accident.

"Anyway, having unleashed the potential for infinite creativity Universal Intelligence created us and all other intelligent life forms so it could continue its expansion. Indeed that is the only reason Universal Intelligence created us."

"How so?" we asked more or less in unison.

"Since Universal Intelligence could not experience itself as itself, it created us so that it could continue to experience itself through us in ever expanding ways, in tune with the expanding universe. That is what is meant when we say that God is our Father and we are the son of God.

"Now, here's where it gets interesting," said Harley, leaning over to get closer to us as if he was about to share something of great value. "Without us, God isn't."

"I don't get it. What are you saying, Harley?" I said.

"Look, Jack, I think you are trying to make it too difficult," said Harley, somewhat impatiently. "It's really quite simple. God created us and gave us the ability to go in and out of that world of duality and physicality....."

"You mean the world of form that arose out of that first thought and the subsequent Big Bang?" I interrupted.

"Exactly," said Harley, continuing. "..... so it could experience that world vicariously through us. That way Universal Intelligence would continue to expand in tune with the physical universe.

"We are vital to that expansion, Jack. Each and every soul who incarnates and all of those who, like your team here, support that process, is playing a vital role in expanding God's consciousness. That's what I mean when I say that without us, God isn't. Without you, Jack, God isn't."

"So, once I take on a human body, I am God in physical form playing in the physical realm. Is that right?"

"Yes," Harley confirmed. "It is as if the hand of God has put on a glove – and you are that glove. Without that glove Universal Intelligence could not experience the physical world. What a gift you are to God."

"It certainly puts this whole thing into perspective," I ventured. "Wow, little old me helping to expand the mind of God.

Oops! Listen to me. I am beginning to use human languaging already!"

"You might as well get used to it," said Harley. "They have some pretty bizarre notions down there of what God is, most notably the idea that it is some kind of bearded humanoid who spends all his time judging people and thinking up various kinds of punishment for those who break his rules. Weird, I know but you'll find that all out for yourself. For a while at least you might find yourself buying in to that idea."

"Oh come on, Harley," I said. "There's no way I would see that which we know to be the pure essence of unconditional LOVE as a judgmental, angry, dualistic and divisive entity, human or otherwise!"

"Don't depend on it," said Harley. "You'll be amazed at what sounds like good sense when you get down there! Anyway, let's get back to your preparation for the human life experience. Are you clear now why you are doing it and what it's all about?"

"Well, clearer than I was, that's for sure," I responded. "I certainly hadn't any notion of how my journey would be about being in service to the whole idea of Universal Intelligence expanding its consciousness. Up to then I had thought it was more about me as a spiritual being, growing in awareness of what Universal Intelligence—or God—really is."

"That is true too," replied Harley. "But let's talk about that after the break."

8: Personal Soul Growth

Harley appeared again. "OK," he continued. "Let's leave aside the bigger purpose of expanding the mind of God and focus now on what it will do for your own soul growth.

"We've already covered much of it, but I want to bring it together more. As we have said, the whole point is to experience the opposite of LOVE so we can truly experience LOVE at the highest level. It's one thing to know that LOVE is all there is and to take it for granted, but until you have experienced the absence of LOVE, you cannot truly appreciate it—not even up here.

"The same can be said of light. Here we are always in the light, but until you have experienced true darkness, you haven't really experienced the light. Here we take for granted that we are always safe, taken care of, and abundantly supplied with all that we could possibly want or need. But until you have experienced lack and fear, you can hardly know what total safety and abundance mean.

"Well, you're going to get a taste of all those opposites and at times it won't feel so good. In fact some of it will be so awful you will wish you'd never been born. That's when you'll likely come screaming for some help from the other seven up here. But don't count on it. They'll know that it is precisely those experiences that will give you what you most need. You will feel abandoned and betrayed and you will get to feel the very worst kind of separation – abject loneliness."

"What is loneliness?" I demanded to know. "Harley, I feel as though I am totally ignorant about all the things of which you speak and furthermore, judging by the tone of your voice and your energy field language, they don't sound so good!"

I had noticed that Harley had become more harsh in his manner – almost as if he were trying to make me think twice about the assignment. I was also beginning to have what I was later to recognize as strong feelings, even though at this point I did not have a physical body. As I look back now, I see that my vibration was slowing down even more than before and my energy field was becoming denser than I had ever experienced.

The fact that I was already experiencing some feeling sensation and the beginning of emotions in response to what Harley was saying and how he was saying it, was a pretty good indication that my more subtle bodies were already forming. The Causal Body was for sure, since that one is totally connected to Universal Intelligence all the time, but it looked like the Mental and Emotional Bodies were beginning to coalesce into coherent energy patterns as well.

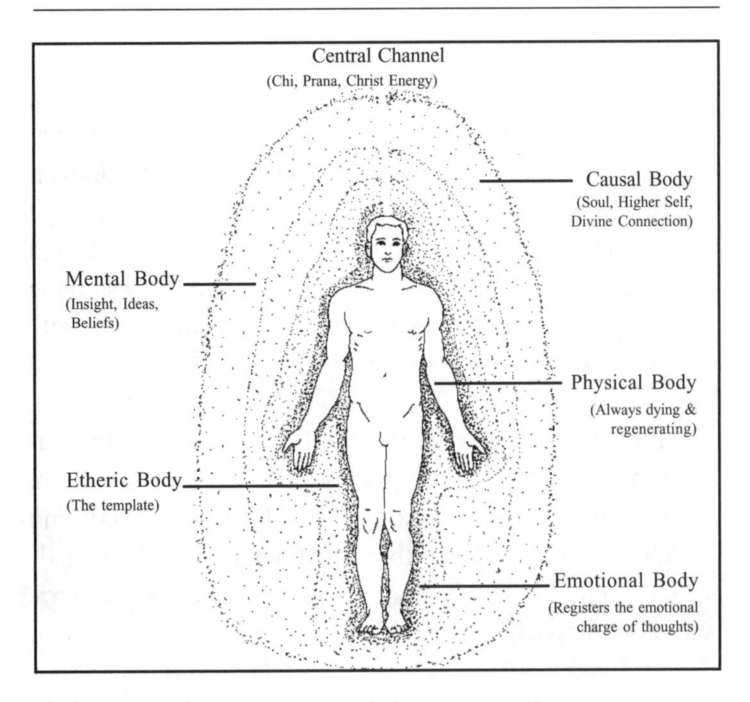

Fig 1: Energy Bodies

"You'll be fine, Jack," said Harley. "But you're looking tired. Probably because your bodies are beginning to form and their heaviness is pulling on you. Let's call it quits for now on this stuff."

Harley must have noticed my feeling state. He probably felt it best not to push me too far yet. There were lots of preparatory lessons to be gone through before I was to go in through the portal. He didn't want me to be too much in my feelings too early. That could create some problems up here. This is not a world of feelings – thought forms only if you please!

"Let's go and get your Divine blueprint," said Harley. "All the numerology has been coded in along with the astrological data, so it's all good to go. Once we get that all properly aligned in your causal, mental and emotional bodies, we can begin your preparation. You will spend some 'nows' in class going through all the aspects of your incarnation. Then we'll program each of the chakras in the etheric body field in order to establish the blueprint for the physical body. That of course will only manifest the moment you incarnate."

We teleported to the place where I was to receive the programming. It didn't take very long and I wasn't really aware of very much happening, except that I was now becoming even more aware of my vibration having slowed down. It was a strange sensation. I had never even been aware of my vibratory rate before.

"Get some rest," said Harley. "You'll need it. You start your classes tomorrow. After that, we will begin the process of choosing your parents! Good night."

Strange. I hadn't heard Harley, or anyone else for that matter speak of tomorrow. Up to now it had only been 'now.' Everything is getting more peculiar by the minute – there I go again! This time thing is really starting to become real for me.

9: Choosing Parents

Choosing my parents was going to be important. I knew that. From them I would get most of my basic character. But that wasn't the end of it. In fact it was probably the least important part of the choice.

More important would be the kind of parents they would be for me–what experiences they would provide for me to learn from and perhaps even more important, what generational baggage they would pass on to me to carry and hopefully transform. All of that would have to align with the mission I would have, if any, and what Harley felt were the most important lessons I had to learn.

I said *if any* with regard to my mission because it was my belief that not every soul goes in with a particular mission predecided. They may acquire one along the way, it's true, but for the majority I would say it's simply a question of doing the life experience, participating in it fully, and showing up. By showing up, I mean opening the heart and taking advantage of this one opportunity to experience existence emotionally.

That dimension is not available in this world because we don't have bodies and therefore don't have feelings. By showing up and participating we are automatically doing what is required, as Harley was, once again, about to remind me.

"Hello, Jack," said Harley. "How are you feeling today? We covered a lot of ground yesterday *(I noticed he was using 'time' related words again),* so it wouldn't surprise me if you were tired or even somewhat confused. Are you?"

"I am a little weary, but I don't feel confused," I said. "I think I have it pretty well organized in my mind."

"Well, let me repeat it for you one more time—just to make sure," said Harley. "The basic aim of taking this human journey is to experience the opposite of what we know to be the truth up here – ONENESS and LOVE. Through the experience of those opposites we can come to know ONENESS and LOVE more fully and through that awareness move to a whole new level in our spiritual growth and expand even more the consciousness of Universal Intelligence. With me up to now, Jack?"

"Sure."

"You also will recall that the human experience will set you up to be abandoned, rejected, betrayed, terrorized, and even tortured during your earth walk. Those are just some examples of things that will help you fully experience the opposites of LOVE and ONENESS. OK, Jack?"

"Well, I guess it's OK. Can't say I'm looking forward to all that though."

"Hey, don't imagine that life is only that," Harley warned. "A great deal of the human experience is totally wonderful and marvelous. In fact I would venture to say that the majority of it is this way. There are many wonderful opportunities to experience LOVE and bliss, harmony and peace in every day.

"We shall see later, these high vibration experiences are just as important to our spiritual growth as the seemingly less pleasant experiences. In fact, there may come a time when, having transcended and given up the victim archetype, we will derive the greatest spiritual growth not from adversity and pain but from the experience of beauty, compassion, gratitude and other wonderful things that feed the spirit.

"However, at this time all humans are, by their own choice, still addicted to victimhood, pain and suffering so it's to there that the energy naturally flows. Since it is a principle that spiritual growth occurs wherever the energy is most in motion, humans will still tend to use these as their catalysts for growth rather than the more positive experiences. Maybe that will change soon and they will be able to choose experiences based in joy and harmony as their catalyst for growth.

"Of course, whether it changes or not is inconsequential to us in this world, Jack. We up here, you see, are not attached to what kind of experiences they use to create growth. Our only concern is that growth occurs and that it leads to a clear remembrance of who we are and expands the consciousness of ONENESS.

"Their current focus on the seemingly negative experiences just reflects the prevailing human appetite for the energy attached to pain and suffering—and especially that associated with victimhood. Wherever the energy is, we follow. That's how it is!

"Anyway, we like for these experiences to come fairly early in childhood so they get firmly implanted before the mind has a chance to rationalize them away or defend against the experience in some other way. In this way we set up a chain of unconsciously self-created repetitions of the same wound over and over again.

"For example, if a child feels it was abandoned in childhood it will simply replay that same scenario over and over in all subsequent relationships. Similarly, the ideas that the child formed in response to that wound – like 'I am worthless, undeserving, unlovable, not OK, etc.,' will be reinforced over and over again until it becomes the belief that drives his/her life. There will be so much pain attached to that toxic idea that it will drive some people to alcohol, drugs or some other addiction that they hope will medicate the pain.

"If everything goes according to plan, this negative belief will create so many blocks in their lives they will in the end be forced to confront it and to heal it. And it is in the process of doing the healing work that the real spiritual work is done. You'll learn more about that later—it's too complicated to explain now.

"Here's the point though: who better to give you the initial experience of separation than your parents?

"The very act of giving birth is an act of separation and for many people the birth trauma alone is sufficient to set off the chain reaction. Other souls choose to have their learning experiences a little later, say at age five or six or in the early 'teen' years.

"Others choose to do it the other way around. They choose parents who will give them a 'nice' upbringing so they develop a false sense of security and then BAMM! The lesson comes when they least expect it – ironically just after they have prayed for spiritual growth."

"I guess that prayer is the signal the Higher Self waits for," I offered. "Right?"

"Absolutely!" said Harley. "The Higher Self loves to hear that prayer. You can just imagine him or her jumping up and down singing and dancing, *He prayed for spiritual growth; he prayed for spiritual growth! Hey, got to call my partner and tell him. Where's my cell phone? Hey Ego. Guess what? The prayer came this morning. Yep! That's right. I have it right here on the record 'Please God, give me spiritual growth.' Come on, let's give him what he wants."*

We all had a good laugh at Harley's attempt at being a ham and he enjoyed the acknowledgment.

"Anyway, no matter how it all comes about," he went on, "it all works just as it should although it does at least to some extent, depend on how it was all set up in the first place at this end. For example, if there was a mission decided upon prior to the incarnation the two guides must set things up so that everything comes together in just the right way and at the correct 'now.'

"Like Princess Di's mission – to open the heart chakra of England," I volunteered. "Her whole life was a preparation for her to achieve that at the moment of her death. Right, Harley?"

"Exactly right," Harley confirmed. "Every circumstance of her life, from the emotionally starved home life; the apparently ridiculous wedding which was doomed from the start; Prince Charles's cold hearted treatment of her; the hounding by the paparazzi — it was all perfect. That was an exceptionally well executed mission. I wish I had been in charge of that one myself but I was otherwise engaged."

"But not everyone comes in with a mission in advance, do they?" I asked, seeking confirmation.

"That's right. You don't necessarily need to have a specific mission. In fact, only a relative few are given that kind of opportunity." There was that stare again! It was just as unnerving as the last two times he bore down on me that way. "The others are just in there contributing to the overall mission of expanding consciousness."

He stared even more intently now than ever before. He said nothing for what seemed like a long time. I held his gaze and tried hard not to measure the time it was taking. I longed to consult that Rolex thought form, but I dared not. It was a really tense moment and what followed didn't reduce my anxiety one little bit.

"Jack," he said slowly and deliberately and with gravity in his voice. "You have been selected for a very important mission. I can't tell you what it is to be just yet. In fact, even I do not know the full details myself, but it is a big one, Jack. I realize that not knowing is going to make it doubly difficult for you in the 'nows' ahead and as we do the classes, but there's no other way, I'm afraid. Even I am somewhat in the dark about it at this moment."

Oh my God, I thought. If even Harley doesn't know the full extent of it, that must mean it has come down from angels up above him. He usually is the one to decide on a soul mission. This was obviously a special case and I wasn't liking it.

"We normally do the selection of parents at the beginning and I was planning to do that next, but I have been told that in your case we will have to leave it almost to the last.

"One of the reasons for that, Jack — and you're probably not going to like this — is that you might be doing two lifetimes concurrently–parallel lives, so to speak. That means a great deal more preparation and planning. Two blueprints to prepare and to align energetically and so on. In the meantime though, Jack, you must proceed with your regular training."

I was spinning again but trying not to repeat my last performance of going off whizzing around the Universe in a burst of chaotic electron activity.

"Parallel lives! Two lives lived concurrently? What is that about?" I was talking more to myself than to Harley. Then I turned and spoke directly to him. "I have heard of such a thing and know that some advanced souls do that occasionally. But me? Come on Harley, tell me that you're kidding. You are, aren't you?"

"I couldn't be more serious, Jack. It's happening. We've checked the Akashic Records and you are perfect for the job. You have all the requirements and you are right for the mission.

"You're just going to have to trust us on this, Jack. Take a brief vacation somewhere out in the cosmos, anywhere you can relax and gather some energy. Let's meet again in a few 'nows,' after you have collected yourself. You need to begin your training classes immediately after that though. There apparently is some urgency about this incarnation so your program is being given a high priority. Good luck, Jack!"

Harley vanished. I went whizzing again. "Well—what would you have done under the circumstances?"

PART TWO:

Incarnation School

10: Pain in the Bank

When I arrived for my first class on Human Dynamics, I was both surprised and disappointed that Harley was not going to be the teacher. As I thought about it of course, it was not in the least bit surprising. Harley was a very senior Angel of Incarnation—though not senior enough apparently to have control over what my incarnation might involve. Obviously there would be others of less seniority who were adequate to the task of teaching the basic training classes and to whom he would delegate those jobs.

It occurred to me that I might not see Harley again for a while; not until the time came for him to reveal my double mission, perhaps.

I had taken his advice and given myself some rest and relaxation in a nice quiet corner of the Universe, where I could ponder my assignment.

It took me quite a while before I could grasp the fact that I was being selected for something really important. What could it be? Harley had mentioned that he had been looking through the Akashic Records. What had he seen, I wonder? I haven't incarnated before so it couldn't be anything to do with a past life, I thought.

On the other hand, though I have no recollection of it, I do believe that I was once a member of a soul team acting in support of a soul who did incarnate, though I have no idea who it was or what the mission was. I might even have done it more than once for all I know. When each assignment is over, all information relevant to that incarnation is erased from the memories of the team members, so how would I know? Maybe they keep that kind of stuff in the Akashic Records though, for precisely this kind of thing.

Well, I suppose Harley will tell me in the end. In the meanwhile I must go through all the basic classes in preparation for my incarnation which I am now beginning to wonder whether I even want. However, there's no going back now, so I might just as well get on with it and be patient. All will be revealed in good time, I presume.

A teacher angel appeared in the room and stood before us. She was very beautiful and radiated white light. Her name was Jeni. She beamed light to us and made a point of welcoming us each by name.

"This class is the first of a number that fall under the general heading of Human Dynamics, 101," Jeni began. "Don't worry about the title—it's just a fancy name for how human beings create their lives for the purposes you've already discussed at some length with Harley.

"The session for today is entitled, *'Pain in the Bank.'* You'll see why in a moment. Harley dubbed it that—you've experienced his sense of humor already, haven't you?"

"Yes, we have," I replied. "We have come to know him quite well in just a very short number of 'nows.' We are very fond of him."

"I'm not surprised," said Jeni. "He is revered by everyone and very well respected too.

"What we are going to look at in this class is how the unhealed pain of each generation is passed on down the line for at least seven generations, thereby becoming part of the individual's consciousness at the moment of birth. This material is passed down through the genes and also gets downloaded to succeeding generations from the Collective Unconscious.

"Now remembering what Harley has already told you, this is purposeful in the sense that it provides energy in the bank so to speak. As soon as you arrive on the earth plane you already have a whole lot of stuff to start working with. Very convenient, don't you think, Jack?"

Jeni did not wait for my answer and for that I was grateful. I'm not sure I understood why it was convenient. I hoped she was going to explain further. At least I got the meaning of Harley's title and play on words, 'Pain in the Bank,' and had to smile to myself.

"It's convenient at two levels," said Jeni obviously picking up on my thoughts.

"First, as I have already said, it provides a number of issues, both large and small, personal and collective, to begin working on right away. For some, there will be enough 'meat' in what they get handed from their ancestors that their need for further lifetime material in the early years of life will be virtually nil. Consequently, they won't need their parents to abandon them or abuse them in order to experience separation first hand. It's already there in the generational baggage handed on down to them and they will process and grow through transforming that.

"Secondly,—and this is related to the first point—when the original pain was first experienced it may have been just too much for those ancestors to deal with at the time. Being so traumatic, they might not have been able to use the experience as an opportunity for growth for them personally.

"So they repressed it and in doing so, put it in the bank so to speak, knowing that a future generation might be able to use it more profitably and at the same time release the held energy around the situation.

"I am sure that would have been the case with the many millions who fell at the hands of Stalin and Hitler during the Second World War. All that is still being worked out, of course, by the succeeding generations most visibly, perhaps, in Israel. The Jews, who have for so long been identified as the victim, are now getting an opportunity to feel what it's like to be a perpetrator. That might be balancing the energies there a little bit. But there are still plenty of opportunities left in that situation for more growth and for the eventual transformation of the energies. I know there are a lot of souls working on doing just that.

"Thirdly, it gives a lot of souls reason to incarnate. They see a whole lot of energy stuck around things that happened many generations back that are still being acted out by the current generation, so they volunteer to come in to work with and transform those fear-based energies into LOVE. It becomes their mission. Harley often describes this irreverently as a 'turn-key' mission or a mission 'franchise.' Everything is all set up for you. Just show up and do the work! That Harley; isn't he a trip?"

We all nodded in agreement and I took the opportunity to make a contribution. "It's my understanding that many of the wars on the planet have their origins in events that occurred many generations back. Those would make ideal 'turn-key' missions, wouldn't they?"

"Yes, indeed," replied Jeni. "They give many opportunities for souls to come in and work with those energies. Ireland is a typical example of that. So was Kosovo.

"The Kosovo war originated in the seventeenth century when, during the Crusades, the Serbian army was slaughtered on the Field of the Blackbirds. *'Remember the Field of the Blackbirds,'* became their battle cry for all subsequent wars. Almost every conflict in the region has had some connection to that field and the war in Kosovo was no exception. Clearly, the unresolved energies attached to that event were being acted out once again."

"Can we assume that some souls have made it their mission to go in and use that war as a way to transform the energy?" I asked.

"Yes, Jack. I do believe that a very large number of souls did go in with that in mind. They would have dispersed themselves around among both the Serbian and Albanian population, preparing for this event for all of their lives. Many of them are still there, I would imagine, hopefully working it all through.

"I did hear about one soul, who was an American and a Catholic priest, who when he received guidance about what was about to happen in Kosovo, travelled there some while beforehand and took with him a small wooden 'Peace Pole.' (*Peace Poles like this were available in America carrying the inscription, 'May Peace Prevail on Earth,'*). His aim was to plant this Peace Pole in the center of the Field of the Blackbirds, so it would act like an acupuncture needle in the earth.

"Just like an acupuncture needle in a human body balances the chi energy in the body, he intended for the Peace Pole to do the same in that precise area of Mother Earth. He had hoped that it would release the pent up, fear-based, energy located there and prevent the war, but clearly it did not. It may nevertheless have helped a great deal to create the circumstances for the transformation to occur when the time is right. You never really know how the things you do out of loving intention will affect things in the physical world. The only thing you can do is to be LOVE and while your heart is open, do what feels right.

"Another example of the 'franchise mission' is when souls go in to release the energy around dark secrets. Child sexual abuse and incest are great examples of this dynamic. Each succeeding generation takes on the pain of the previous generations but then fails to transform it into LOVE because the subject is never broached.

"It remains a secret both within the families where it occurs and in society generally. I know that a vast number of souls have recently volunteered to have their mission be to go in as either victim or perpetrator and in some cases both, so that sexual abuse can all be brought to the light and transformed. They are getting a whole lot of growth out of that experience."

"What about the war on cancer. Isn't the same thing happening there, Jeni?" I asked.

"Absolutely," Jeni agreed. "What is happening there is quite fascinating. Seeing the opportunity to use cancer as an analogy for how, just as cancer cells eat away at and destroy their host, people are actually destroying their own body (Planet Earth) through their greed and disrespect, a vast number of souls volunteered for this mission. The idea was to demonstrate to humans how deadly was their belief in and preoccupation with everything that was not LOVE.

"The souls would focus their efforts in those areas of the world where greed was the main motivation behind every facet of life and each of them would volunteer to get cancer. The reason they would do this is because, just as humans have tried to solve problems by aggression and hate, humans have tried to do the same with cancer. They have 'made war' on cancer. The have developed weapons to 'beat' cancer. And of course, it hasn't worked—in spite of the billions of dollars they have thrown at the problem.

"The reason it hasn't worked is because souls have volunteered to demonstrate that such strategies don't work for cancer any more than they work for life in general. To prove this, they deliberately defy the drugs and other aggressive treatments and succumb to death.

At the same time other souls have volunteered to contract cancer too, but they refuse medical treatment and instead bring Universal LOVE into their bodies through spiritually based treatments—and get well.

"The lesson is, of course, that only LOVE heals. LOVE is the answer to every problem, but humans are so fear based still, they don't get it. By demonstrating this truth with the most feared of all diseases and against which medical technology has been 'battling' for so long, the souls are hoping to wake them up to this truth."

11: America's Bank Account

After the break Jeni shifted gears. "Jack, I under stand from Harley that you are going to incarnate into a lifetime located in the United States, at least for one of them, so we ought to look at some examples of repressed generational pain that are relevant to that country and culture."

Her reference to my dual incarnation was not lost on me. Jeni obviously knew that I was going to do the parallel lives deal. I wonder how much she knows? She can't know more than Harley and even he doesn't know everything; at least he didn't when we last spoke.

Jeni began, "Let's just enumerate some of the main themes of generational pain that are common to all the people who live in America and then give examples of the kind of pain that typically gets passed on from within individual families and to which you might perhaps find yourself subjected in your own life experience.

"It is important to remember that for the most part this kind of pain is very deep down in the collective psyche and is not subject to awareness. Most people will deny that it is a part of who they are and do not see that each generation is acting out the pain of their ancestors up to seven generations back.

"Repression is the subject of a later class, but basically the idea is that in order to avoid feeling intense feelings, such as guilt, hurt, rage and shame, we push them down deep into our unconscious mind and out of awareness. However, that doesn't mean to say that they remain inactive. On the contrary, these feelings continue to put out energy such that people continue to act them out in all sorts of different ways, albeit without awareness of what they are doing. This applies to the big collective issues as well as to the more privately held ones. That said, let's now list a few of the major ones that reside in the American psyche.

"One that goes back a long way is the shame the descendents of white settlers feel for the way the indigenous people of America were—and are still being treated. The white people lied, cheated and reneged on virtually every agreement they ever struck with the indigenous people. They robbed them of their land and their livelihood and committed genocide against them on a large scale. They rounded them up in their thousands and marched them to reservations on lands that the whites didn't want. To this day they keep them poor, dependent on government handouts and marginalized. The Native American for his part remains totally stuck in anger and victimhood.

"Obviously, there remains a lot of opportunity here for souls who are attracted to missions of this kind and a lot to be done by way of transformation of this issue.

"You know, Jack, everything is perfect but from our point of view, it is sad that the older generations of Native Americans are dying out and taking with them a spiritual wisdom that would really help transform the planet. They knew the truth. The white man has nothing to match it and the younger generation of Native Americans may not have had the opportunity to be well enough initiated into it to take the wisdom forward."

Jeni was a fast talker and even though she said she was happy to answer questions, it was hard to get anything in. I seized an opportunity when she had to pause to clear her speaking channel.

"Jeni, I'm not sure I understand how that kind of pain continues to be acted out. Can you explain how that works, please?"

"Well, one way to act this out is to continue to abuse these people and deny them their rights as citizens while at the same time finding apparently sound economic and rational arguments to support that kind of action. That form of acting out keeps the perpetrators in denial about the original crime and all subsequent ones and takes away their guilt—temporarily at least—by giving a 'reason' for what happened. The Native Americans continue to create these circumstances in order to support their being right about being 'no good,' 'not worthy' and victimized. You can see how, by continuing to act it out, nothing changes. No transformation at all — just stuck energy.

"Another way that it gets acted out by white people is through their appropriating the Native people's spirituality. Whites think they are honoring the indigenous people and thereby healing the pain, but in reality they are stealing the only thing the Native Americans have left of any value. I'm not sure how the Native Americans are creating it on their side, but clearly they are. Otherwise it wouldn't be occurring."

"So what you are saying is that both parties in any situation bear responsibility for co-creating the situation," I suggested, looking for confirmation. "And that, in the beginning at least, it was created for a reason, like for the spiritual growth of the group soul or a healing through transformation. Is that correct, Jeni?"

"Yes, that is exactly right. But because it gets crystallized as generational baggage, nothing changes from generation to generation. Furthermore, the opportunities for healing and transformation that were there in the first place for the original people have all but disappeared. That's when it becomes really counterproductive, not only in human terms but in our terms as well.

"We have no interest in energy getting stuck to that degree, except inasmuch as it provides ready made 'turn-key' missions for souls who want to see if they can break the deadlock. Even so, we would rather all souls were able to have their experiences, learn their lessons quickly and transform the energy right away. It is much more efficient that way and energy will not get stuck. Fortunately, human beings are getting better in this regard and have lately been able to move through their personal issues relatively quickly. But not so with generational pain.

"Take, for example, the other really obvious example of pain being passed on from one generation to the next — the repressed guilt and anger over the slavery issue. No one is apparently willing to try to transform this one and it just goes on and on being acted out ad infinitum. Once again, lots of opportunities here for souls who want to incarnate into this mess!

"Obviously, Jack, this goes very deep and the pain on both sides is intense. Guilt and anger — and there's a tremendous amount of it just under the surface, being acted out in a lot of different ways but festering nevertheless like a dormant volcano. One day it will blow and then energy will fly!

"Race is a factor in almost every facet of American life. But it doesn't get dealt with except at a very superficial level. The core issue of slavery is hardly touched so it is like a cancer eating away at society. Whatever the gift will be in the situation for both the white and black races I don't know, but it must be something really big for both.

"Anyway, I know that this race thing is going to be a big part of your experience, Jack — it's bound to be for any soul incarnating into the American culture — so I'm not going to say any more about this one. It is big, though. If you get to be a black person in your upcoming incarnation you will certainly have to deal with issues of being less than, being rejected and discriminated against so it is a great opportunity to experience these particular lessons. Are you up to having a black incarnation, Jack?"

"That's a thought," I replied. "I wonder if that's what Harley has in mind for me? He's talking about some important mission so maybe I'm going in as a black person to help heal that pain. What do you think Jeni?"

"Harley hasn't shared with me anything about your incarnation. That is unusual. He generally tells me everything and even if he doesn't I can usually read his mind. But this time I couldn't. So maybe you're right. It's true that this issue has been fertile ground for a whole lot of valuable lessons for countless souls, but it's gone on long enough. The energy is stuck and when that happens people get stuck in the story too and that's not good.

"So maybe its time America saw another powerful spirit like Martin Luther King Jr., or Malcom X to move the energy that is stuck around this issue. It's going to take someone of that caliber to heal the slavery issue and all that has followed in its wake. You have the potential, Jack. Do you know that?"

"I'm not sure that I do," I replied. "I have always thought of myself as quite ordinary, really."

"Well, you're not ordinary. Your heart is very strong and you have a lot of LOVE. Harley sees that in you I know. That's why he wants you to do something special. It would take a soul with a lot of LOVE to clean that issue out of the American psyche, because for sure you would have a tremendous amount of negative, fear-based energy projected onto you. The only antidote there is for that is LOVE and clearly you have a lot of that. Own it Jack."

I looked around at my team. They were all nodding in agreement and smiling.

"We'd love to support you in that role Jack" they all agreed. "We know you could do it."

"Thanks, guys. And thank you, Jeni. I guess I needed to hear that. I will try to own it more. However, this is still only conjecture. Nothing has yet been mentioned about such an assignment though I must say the idea excites me. I am getting a strong deja vu feeling that I might have been on Malcom's team. It seems right," I said.

"Be that as it may," said Jeni, " we must bring our focus back to the class. We have a lot to get through yet.

"So, to finish up on the collectively held issues in the American psyche, we might mention the shared pain that is still held about the McCarthy era. There was a tremendous amount of shame involved in that awful episode of American history. You'll see it being acted out again in your time too, Jack, which means, of course, that the shame still lives in the shadow part of the American psyche—waiting to be healed. They'll call it patriotism, but it is the same thing. You will see the government trying to take away civil liberties just like McCarthy did.

"And we shouldn't leave this topic without mentioning the wound that every American feels about the Vietnam War. It was one of the most awful mistakes that America ever made and people everywhere felt great shame over it.

"There's a whole lot more that we could enumerate, but they are nothing in comparison to the issues we have just mentioned.

"Let's now move to the other kinds of generational pain that gets transferred down the ancestral line. Primary among these is the whole issue of child abuse, especially child sexual abuse. Again this is a very powerful field for learning the opposite of LOVE, but to the extent that it is being passed on down through the generations—with victims becoming perpetrator in a never ending spiral—it indicates once again that the energy has become stuck, and that's not good.

"However, I do understand from the angel who oversees that area of human experience that a whole army of volunteers has incarnated with the intention of participating in that particular form of human interaction either as a victim or as a perpetrator. Some will experience incest, others will know what it is to be violated sexually and so on.

"The idea is that so much of it will occur in all its forms and at all levels of society, including the established churches, that it will come out into the light. It will cause a lot of pain but as awareness grows people will make the decision not to pass it on any more."

"Will that mean that souls will no longer be able to choose sexual abuse as their way to experience separation?" I asked.

"Not necessarily," replied Jeni. "But it will enable the dam that has held centuries of generational pain around this issue to break open so that the energy tied up there can flow. Individual souls may still choose it but not out of obligation to carry it on from the past and into the future.

"In any case, spiritual growth no longer needs to be hard, so we can definitely lighten up on the lessons. It is probably time to stop using sexual abuse as a way to experience separation. There are plenty of other options that will get us to the same place and a lot quicker too."

12: Past Life Carry-over

Jeni reappeared and immediately began the class on past life carry-over. I had assumed this to be similar to the idea of pain being brought forward from previous generations, except in this case it had bled through from a past life. I was to learn that it wasn't that simple.

"I think you already heard from Harley that a lot of humans believe in the idea of past lives—meaning that we incarnate over and over again, one life after another. He also pointed out I'm sure, that, since there is no such thing as time, past or future has no meaning. Therefore there can't be any such thing as a past life.

"The idea of past lives is a particularly human construct, devised mainly as a way for humans to feel that they continue as individual souls, thereby doing a bypass around the idea that they don't exist. The Ego has sold them on the idea of their existence separate from the All-That-Is, that they have created this notion that they go from one incarnation to the next maintaining their individuality and separateness.

"I know this all sounds strange to you, Jack, but I can only explain it to you as they understand it, not as we know it to be in our reality. The whole point of you learning this stuff anyway is so that it will seem to make sense to you while you are human, so let me tell you how it is for them.

"There is no doubt that many people have the 'experience' of remembering a past life and that there is, in that moment, a feeling of certainty that they were there in another lifetime, even in a specific historical context, and that the content of that life has specific meaning to their current life experience. There is no doubt that a past life experience like this can seem real to them. And, since they can only relate things to time and space and to individual existence, it makes sense to them to think of it as themselves having a 'past' life. Some people even talk about 'future' lives and 'in-between' lives."

"This sounds like it could be tricky," I observed. "Can you explain this a little more?"

"Yes, it really is one of the more tricky aspects of being human," Jeni replied. "The trap that a lot of people fall into is to use the idea of past lives as a distraction from the current lifetime experience. They use it as an avoidance strategy. But you are an old soul, Jack, so I feel confident that you will not get sidetracked by them. You will live in the 'now.'"

"Nevertheless, I would like you to explain this a little more to me," I requested, "so I can better understand the difference between how we see things and how I will see them when I am a human."

"Certainly," said Jeni. "Another way of looking at this is to return to our ocean and wave analogy. A wave may seem to rise in time and fall in time, but a wave is forming and dying in the same moment. At every moment it is dying back into the ocean, into the truth of what it is – just water in motion, driven by the wind. The wave was always simply an illusion. It makes no sense to speak of the last wave, or the next wave. A wave just is in that moment. However, the same water molecules can just as easily become put in motion in the next moment too and once again seem to be a wave. It might even appear to be the 'next' wave, but in reality it is just the water in motion.

wave/ ocean

"Your Higher Self, Jack, will troll the vast ocean of consciousness — rather like most humans now do with the worldwide web — to find an experience that fits your need in that moment and will bring it forth for you as a memory trace. The purpose may be to help you learn something about your present circumstance that you would not learn in any other way, or to clear some stuck energy. A lot of times a soul will search through the ocean of consciousness, sometimes referred to as the Akashic Records, to find something specific to bring forth as 'past life baggage.' This has much the same value as bringing forth generational baggage as we discussed in the last session."

"OK, I think I have it now," I said. "Thanks for the explanation."

That being the end of this lesson, we took a break.

13: Perception Is Everything

My lesson on how humans perceive the world turned out to be a fascinating one. I had no idea how different everything would be once I became a human.

"Jack, you will be amazed at how real everything will seem to you when filtered through the five senses that come with the human body," Jeni began. "Their senses are attuned to a very narrow band of vibration so they can only perceive the world in a limited way. That's why they cannot see us, for instance. We move around them all the time, but they don't know that.

"What we know as simply vibrations, they see and feel as solid objects in space and, because they trust their senses so much, they imagine that anything that cannot be seen, heard, felt, smelled or tasted doesn't exist. They have invented wonderful ways to magnify the senses and in some cases extend the bandwidth but for the most part their senses keep them very limited and restricted to physical reality only. This is purposeful of course, in order to keep up the illusion of separateness and belief in the body."

"Harley had mentioned," I interrupted, "that since the Harmonic Convergence, more and more people were finding themselves with what he called *'extra sensory perception.'* Can you explain that, Jeni?"

"Yes, this is called ***Multi Sensory Reality,*** " replied Jeni. "A lot of humans have raised their vibration enough to develop sensory awareness beyond the limitations of the five senses. Examples of this include, intuition, psychic awareness, clairvoyance and other types of extra 5-sensory perception. Multi sensory awareness is becoming more commonplace among the people.

"This is all part of Spirit's plan, of course, to have people awaken. As we keep on stressing, Universal Intelligence gave humans free will so it remains up to them when — and even whether — to wake up. But by giving them the tools to see beyond 5-sensory reality, UI is giving them a nudge in the right direction, so to speak. Does this answer your question, Jack?"

"Yes, thank you," I replied.

'The part that humans have yet to realize," Jeni continued, " is the extent to which they actually create what they see. Their belief is that perception is one way — that information about the outside world is fed through their sensory system and they perceive whatever it is. That is not how it works.

"Human scientists now know that the world that they perceive as 'out there' is a projection of mass consciousness, but that idea has a long way to go before it is accepted by the majority.

Fig. 2: Reality Projected

"I think Harley has already told you that when you get down there, we have set it up that you will not be aware that the world you will see out there will simply be a reflection of how mass consciousness makes it up to be. Correct?"

"Yes, Harley did say that, and I understand that it will be that way." I responded.

"Not only that," Jeni countered, "you may, along with quite a number of people who are beginning to find out that they can in fact manifest things in the physical world and manipulate time and space through thought, begin to play with the idea and find out that you have a lot of power to create in the world. You will enjoy discovering that power. Let's now go on to lesson five which looks at shadow stuff."

14: Shadow Stuff

Beginning the class, Jeni said, "Harley has already explained to you that the point of the human journey is to experience separation so profoundly that when you awaken again to the truth of Oneness, your awareness of and appreciation of it will be magnified thousands of times. Is that how you heard it, Jack?"

"Yes, that's right," I responded. "Harley also told me that my Ego guide will provide me with lots of opportunities to experience separation so that my belief in it will become really solid. That in turn, will give me something to really push against so that when I do break through into the awareness of Oneness, the magnification will be even bigger."

"Good," said Jeni. "You seem to have a good understanding of it. However, I think Harley was referring only to the opportunities to feel separation in what occurs in the outer world. I want to show you how we create the experience of separation within ourselves. I think this was one of Universal Intelligence's great masterpieces."

"Let's return to Harley's concept of 'pain in the bank' As he pointed out, humans are still very much in the place of choosing pain and suffering as a way to learn — and that's their choice which we have to honor. So, naturally the Ego finds all sorts of ways to bank pain. One way to create it, store it up and pay it forward to future generations is through generational pain. Remember that?"

I nodded, but said nothing. I was anxious to hear what she was leading up to.

"Well, humans have a way to bank self-created pain within themselves to create intense ***internal*** separation as well. Isn't that just a wonderful idea?" she smiled.

"Not if you're going to be the one in pain," I countered. "How does that happen?"

"It starts early," replied Jeni. "Whomever you choose to be your parents will teach you what you should like in yourself — because it gets you love and approval — and what you should hate in yourself — which gets you the opposite. You learn to be what's cool and disown what is uncool about you.

"From then on you present to the world only half of what you are. The other, uncool, parts remain buried deep down in your unconscious mind, disowned, denied and totally repressed. As you get older you might discover, or will be shamed into believing other things 'bad' things about yourself. You'll add these to your uncool list and repress them too. A great way to create internal separation, don't you think?"

Dodging the question, I asked, "Wasn't there a very famous psychiatrist and an awakened being who referred to this bank as the shadow?"

"Yes, that was Carl Jung," replied Jeni, recognizing that I wasn't sharing her enthusiasm for creating a shadow full of pain.

COOL		**UNCOOL**
Nice Compliant Quiet Intelligent Generous Pretty Handsome	PERSONAL	Mean Cruel Liar Thief Controlling Ugly Angry
Fits in Integrity Compassionate Patriotic	SOCIETY	Immoral Sexual Pervert Untrustworthy Unpatriotic
Good Citizen Loving Spiritual Saintly Good	ALL HUMANITY	Murderer Rapist Incest Genocide Racial Segregation
IMAGE		**SHADOW**

Fig. 3: The Separation Within

"You will also repress," she went on, " all memories of painful emotional trauma that you were not able to handle at the time. That means a slew of unresolved grief, anger, rage, guilt and shame will lie buried in your shadow, gathering interest in that pain bank of yours, Jack. Actually, I am not sure that's the correct analogy. Perhaps it should be "gathering energy just like a volcano." One day it might blow and all come to the surface.

"Humans are so scared that this might happen and that they might have to face their shadow, they find someone to project it all onto—without awareness of course. They have no idea that they are doing it."

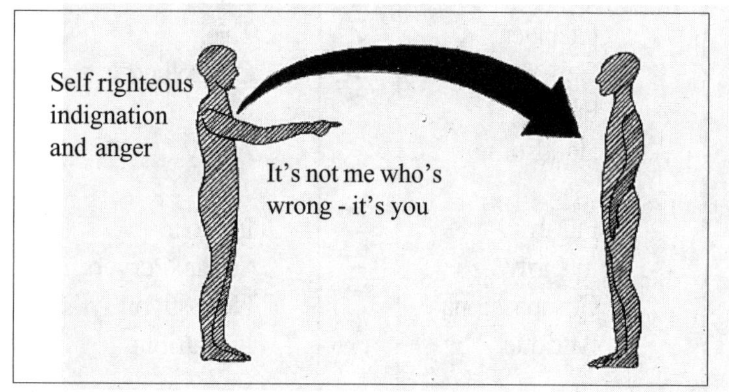

Fig 4: Projection

Jeni looked at me, rather in the same way that Harley did when he began talking about my mission. After a long pause she began.

"From what I understand, this is going to play a very big part in your mission, Jack. Has Harley told you what your mission is yet?"

"No, he hasn't and I am getting very nervous," I answered. " I have a feeling, as we have said before, that it might be the racial healing mission, but that has not been confirmed. I don't know why it is taking so long."

"Neither do I," said Jeni. "However, I do know that projection is going to be an important part of it, not just for yourself, but for a whole group of people. That's what I heard."

"You mean you can project the collective pain of a whole group onto another person, or even another group?" I asked.

"Oh, yes," replied Jeni emphatically. "Look how President Clinton became enraged and morally righteous on behalf of the American people when he saw how Slobodan Milosevic, was ethnically cleansing the Albanians from Kosovo.

"It resonated with America's shadow stuff about their own unresolved guilt for ethnically cleansing the country of the American Indian, so in order to avoid facing that guilt, Clinton on behalf of all Americans, declared Milosovic to be 'the face of Evil,' and felt justified in going to war against him.

"What he didn't understand was that America had actually 'manifested' this dictator and created the whole situation in order to heal its shadow, but it missed the opportunity. It saw only the outward drama and failed to see its meaning."

Jeni once again gave me that long hard stare and made a statement that rocked me. " Remember this well, Jack. I have a feeling that the next opportunity like this could fall to you."

With that Jeni vanished, leaving me feeling very nervous indeed. What had she meant by that? Our lessons were at an end which meant I wouldn't see her again. Bummer!

PART THREE

The Mission

15: Mission Revealed

My basic schooling having come to completion, the moment had come for me to learn about my mission. Truth be told, I was scared stiff. All that I had learned about how things might be in the World of Humanity had made me think twice about even taking on the ordinary human assignment, let alone doing something really special and more than likely extremely challenging.

"Sit down, Jack," Harley commanded in a soft but serious voice. "It's time for us to talk. I have something to tell you which quite frankly surprised the hell out of me when I got it relayed to me from Higher Command."

"Tell me Harley — for God's sake!" I almost screamed. *(Though I was really tense I was not oblivious, even in this moment, of the irony of having made my appeal for something that might make God happier).* "What am I going to be and do?"

"Well, Jack," Harley began, "earlier I told you that it wasn't going to be just one incarnation you were going to have, but two. The idea was that they would be simultaneous. Well, there's been a change of plan. It's now just going to be one."

"Well, that's a relief," I said.

"Wait till you hear the alternative plan," replied Harley. "But I might as well tell you what the first assignment was going to be before they changed everything. I think you had already guessed the essence of it."

"The Malcom X connection?" I countered.

"More or less," replied Harley. "You were going to be born into a very poor black family in the Deep South. Your father was to leave soon after your birth, leaving your mother to raise you in the worst of circumstances. You were to be into drugs, murder, prison – the whole bit; just like thousands of other black people in America. You would have done several years in prison for something you didn't do just so you would become enraged.

"This would have all been in preparation for you to become an activist in a movement that would eventually bring black people together in such a way as to bring enormous change in the situation and would open up the process for healing to take place on a pretty deep level. It would have been a pretty big assignment, Jack."

"Did I do something to lose it, Harley?" I asked gingerly. I wondered whether they may have thought that I wouldn't be up to it.

"Not in the least," said Harley reassuringly. "I think you would have done a great job. You have that kind of heart, Jack. You have that degree of LOVE to be able to carry off that kind of incarnation, so have no concern in that regard. It's just that they felt that you could do something even larger – just as difficult but in a completely different way. They have found someone else for that other job already. There's a strong chance that you might meet him down there. Your mission and his intersect timewise and there might even be interaction between you."

"Come on Harley, out with it! What is my mission? I can't bear the suspense any longer!"

"Your mission is to heal the fractured soul of America and then as a result of that — now get this — bring about world peace and the transformation of the human race."

"What?"

"Your mission is to heal America; bring about world peace and raise the consciousness of the human race."

"Harley, you've got to be joking. I don't even understand what that means!" I was almost hysterical by now. "Why are you doing this to me, Harley? I just wanted an ordinary incarnation. This is way over the top for me!"

"OK, don't panic, Jack. It's all being worked out in advance. We've got a huge team of angels working on it and you're going to have a completely different team assigned to you – all very old souls who will be able to support you every step of the way, so don't look so worried."

I was totally stunned, confused and afraid. Why me, I thought — I don't want this kind of responsibility. I am not an old, experienced soul like the ones Harley had sent down before, so why was I being picked for something so big?

"But what about the other guys who voted for me to go down," I protested. "We've been together a long time."

"Don't worry. They have all been assigned to go with you to play the necessary roles alongside you. You are all going as a team. Besides, there are thousands of souls already down there preparing the ground. These souls are already identified down there as lightworkers and they are doing a huge amount of vital energy work in preparation for this assignment.

"There is also another old and wise soul who is being assigned right now to be the one playing opposite you in the drama that will unfold—the drama that will change everything. He will carry just as much responsibility as you. In fact he may have to endure a much greater degree of negative energy being directed at him than you. But you will have by far the greater challenge in terms of having to exhibit extreme moral and spiritual courage in carrying out your mission."

"But Harley," I interjected. "Why me? I'm not very experienced and have not had sufficient training to qualify me for such an important assignment. There must be others far better qualified. What if I mess this up?"

"Jack, how many more times do I have to tell you that in the end nothing matters? You cannot mess up. Spirit always finds a way to balance it out. It's not about a particular outcome—that's human thinking—but about the process. It is true that this is a huge assignment and you are the right person for the job, Jack, even though you might seem to be not so qualified as some others. In any case there is no one who has the 'right' experience because there is no precedent for this assignment. It has never come up before."

"What do you mean?" I asked.

"Well," Harley began thoughtfully, trying to find words that might make it clear without scaring me even more. "You will recall that Universal Intelligence decided to expand its consciousness by first creating and then experiencing through us the three dimensional world of separation and physical form. Right?"

"Yes, that's as I understand it," I replied.

"Well, it simultaneously foresaw the time when humanity (the souls who were incarnate at the time), would actually awaken from the dream—even while in physical form."

"You mean that they would act there on Earth just like we souls do here?" I ventured. "Like they would always be in a state of LOVE and PEACE instead of fear; in complete harmony and bliss?"

"That's right," said Harley. "They would suddenly realize that separation was just an illusion and that there was no need to be afraid of anything, least of all each other."

"But, I am still confused Harley," I said. "If, as you told me previously that the whole point of creating the illusion of separation was to magnify our appreciation of Oneness, why would you want to blow the illusion now?"

"Because that part is complete," he replied. "Enough souls have been through the experience on Earth to have magnified the awareness of the nature of Oneness, so the expansion of consciousness in that department has been achieved. The need to create separation through wars, strife, hunger, discrimination, torture, abuse, pain and suffering is over."

"So why is it still continuing?" I asked. "Why not just call a halt, declare it all one big fake, and bring everyone home?"

"Because Universal Intelligence is never one to rest up and stop expanding and it doesn't want to miss an opportunity to expand by transforming a situation into something even more wonderful. So, rather than just declare the game over, UI has set it up—and Jack, you're going to love this, it's so elegant —UI is literally planning to continue its experience of itself as itself, but in physical form ***all the time.***

"Why? So it can continue to experience the bliss of existence as a FEELING as well as a KNOWING. Don't you see

Jack? Universal Intelligence will create Heaven on Earth. Is that cool, or what?"

"Let me see if I have this straight," I said. "Up to now, this world—the World of Divine Truth, or the World of Spirit or Heaven even as some humans call it, has been vibrating at a completely different frequency to the world of physical form which we call the World of Humanity. That world is bound in three dimensional reality, time and space. Ours is not. Am I correct so far?"

Harley nodded, but said nothing. I continued to try to get things straight in my mind by articulating the situation as I saw it, for I had a strong feeling that all this was going to be crucial background to my mission.

"Universal Intelligence has completed the phase of consciousness expansion whereby it created through us, as His or Her representatives, the illusion of separation and duality in the World of Humanity. But rather than just bring it to an end, UI wants to merge the two worlds together so that the vibration that we have in this world becomes the vibration of the World of Humanity as well. That way we can all have bodies whenever we want so that we can continue to have the benefit of being able to 'feel' as well as 'know' the bliss of Oneness. It is by merging the two worlds and keeping the benefits of both, that we create Heaven on Earth. Do I have it right, Harley?"

"Pretty much so, I think." Harley replied. "There's a whole lot more to it than that, but that's a pretty good summation.

"However, Universal Intelligence never creates outcomes by decree although, as you know, it has the power to do anything It wants. It could create Heaven on Earth in a nanosecond if It wanted to. With Universal Intelligence, the name of the game is transformation which means that it's the process that counts.

"This is where you come in, Jack. Your role will be to set this whole transformational process in motion. As I have said, the lightworkers have been working hard making preparations, but the things that you do, the circumstances that get created as a result of what you do and the decisions you make will precipitate the collapse of the dream and cause a new reality to dawn. It might not happen during your actual lifetime of course since there are lots of stages to be gone through first to bring people to this new awareness. But then again, it might. You never know. It depends on a great number of factors.

"It probably won't look pretty because, since UI gave free will to every soul to enjoy during its incarnation, there will be millions of people who will put up enormous resistance to the change. They are so addicted to being victims that the idea of there being no right or wrong, no guilt, no blame, no anger etc., will be just too threatening to them. They will group together and create a powerful mass Ego dead set against making the shift. They will use religion as a means of trying to maintain a reality based on separation and specialness and there is a very strong likelihood that there will be many wars on the planet. These will all be part of the transformation process of course, and if that's what it takes to break the illusion, that's what it will take."

16: America's Soul Destiny

Having taken a break, Harley now continued. "Having given you the big picture, let's back up a bit now to the assignment that is specifically to do with the country known as America and the role that you will play in its healing.

"The Awakening is to start in America and will spread out from there. This is the soul destiny of America and everything that it is experiencing 'now' is in preparation for the Awakening.

"However, apart from the lightworkers we have already spoken of, the majority of the population is still asleep and fully committed to the illusion. The people are, on the whole, very religious and many are quite fundamentalist in their beliefs. It will be difficult to awaken those people."

"So, why America, Harley? I interrupted. "Why not other countries, like those in the East? Eastern religions and philosophies seem to be much more in alignment with spiritual truth than the western religions. Wouldn't they be much more likely to awaken quickly? India for example has been the birthplace of so many holy men who have become awakened."

"You're right. Compared with other countries, America is spiritually challenged. It is so bound up with values firmly attached to money, wealth and power that it has very little in the way of a spiritual life. Even the religious life it has revolves around the business of running a church rather than the task of imparting spiritual values to its members or promoting spiritual growth.

"And yet, what makes America so eminently suitable is that it is so pragmatic. It is spiritually immature but it is not hidebound by centuries of culture, tradition, social class and all the other things that tend to make cultures resistant to change. It has very little of any of those things. Change is a way of life in America. It embraces change. It's ability to change makes it flexible and adaptable.

"It is all the more suitable for being a spiritual neophyte. Most of what passes in the World of Humanity for spirituality is pretty much off the mark anyway, so America is better off in this scenario coming from almost nothing. There's less to fight."

"America does have a very strong and deep shadow side to it, about which it is in total denial, doesn't it?" I ventured to add, anxious to show that the lessons on denial, repression and projection had not been wasted on me. I remembered from my lesson with Jeni how America was in total denial about the slavery issue, the Native American holocaust, its dismal human rights record, it's corrupt justice system, the way it's political system is controlled by the corporations and the many other aspects of its shadow it wouldn't look at.

"To say the least," I continued now that I was on a roll, "America does seem unwilling to look at any of its own shadow material and has become a master of projection. It has projected it all onto other people and countries and has become so arrogant and self-righteous. How can we get America to face its own shadow stuff and transform that? Surely it is a prerequisite to awakening, isn't it Harley?"

"Yes, it is," he replied. "But the rest of the world is in denial too. There is not a country in the world which is not passing on centuries of generational pain, guilt and anger—and refusing to own it.

"You mentioned India. Yes, India has produced some wonderful holy men, but India as a whole is trapped in a rigid caste system and a way of thinking that immobilizes its people.

"It is the same in many middle eastern countries too. Even other western countries like those of Europe and England are weighed down by their history and are as spiritually immovable as their stone edifices.

"Many of these old countries tend to be shame-based and their customs, all of which are designed to protect image, keep face, be respectable, do what is expected, stay in line, respect elders, etc., have the effect of reinforcing denial and promoting repression. Breaking through that repression would be difficult.

"It is precisely because America is so spiritually and culturally shallow and a melting pot of cultures and races that it is so perfect for this role of bringing about a shift in global consciousness.

"The only other country that I would say is as open as America and just as ready for a spiritual awakening is Australia—for more or less the same reasons.

"However, the other thing that makes America so perfect at this time is that she has the power to effect great changes simply as a result of being both a military and economic superpower. Whatever America does gets the attention of the whole world. If America were to awaken, I think the whole world would be so amazed it would drop its recently formed hatred of America and follow suit."

17: Prophecies

This was starting to sound familiar to me. "Hasn't this Awakening been foretold on the Earth Plane a number of times, Harley?" I enquired. "And haven't they foretold of great disasters and cataclysmic events happening prior to the Awakening? Around the date 2012, I think I heard one returning soul say. I hope I'm not going to have too much to do with creating that!"

"Yes, that's right, Jack. Throughout history we have sent souls in who were granted limited immunity from the spiritual amnesia requirement and, as a consequence, were able to pierce the veil more or less at will.

"We did that on purpose so these special souls would produce spiritual writings that would span many centuries, represent many diverse cultures and emanate from many different areas of the world, and would foretell of the great Awakening. Each of these 'seers' would all be in broad agreement about what was going to happen.

"Well, they carried out their missions well which meant that their writings showed up in such places as the biblical Book of Revelation as well as the traditional texts of the Mayans, the Hopi Indians and many other indigenous peoples.

"The best known of our brethren who incarnated with this mission and whose predictions have proven to be extremely accurate is Nostradamus. He incarnated in human 'now' time 1503, and foresaw many global events that have already come true and even in the 'now,' continue to unfold as he predicted.

"He not only foretold of both world wars but actually named Hitler and described the swastika. He foretold of the discovery of penicillin, AIDS, the assassination of President Kennedy and the collapse of the Soviet Union. He foretold that the people would elect the 'village idiot' as the leader of the most powerful nation in the early part of the second millennium and foresaw cataclysmic change on a global scale at around the same time, including massive earth changes and violent political upheaval.

"He also spoke of a "King of Terror That Will Come From the Skies." The souls who are incarnate at this 'now' are still trying to decide whether this refers to that event now known as 911, or whether it refers to something worse yet to come. Of course, we know that it will be whatever the souls incarnate at this 'now' decide to create.

"The Hopi Indian soul family has also had many that could see beyond the physical world and see the truth. They too have been extremely accurate in their predictions and have offered humans many a window on the future. They spoke of

Three Great Shakings that would occur at the end of the millennium and the beginning of the next. Scholars have interpreted this to be the First and Second World Wars.

"Our dear soul brother, Edgar Cayce, during his spectacular incarnation made a number of very precise predictions including the stock market crash of 1929 and the Second World War. Many of his predictions for the new millennium concerned political upheaval on a global scale and 'earth changes' that would be cataclysmic in nature.

"In many of the prophecies, the date 2012 is significant, especially in the Mayan and Hopi writings. As you know, Jack, we don't follow calendars, clocks and such things as that because up here there is no time, but since 2012, is not far away and seems likely to coincide with the scenario that UI has in mind for the Awakening, you might be forgiven for thinking that these seers had it about right.

"However, there is one major assumption that humans have made based on those writings, which is erroneous. One who has spotted it is a lightworker known as Gregg Braden, a soul who, by the way, I prepared for his present incarnation. He has figured out that even though all the prophecies have the same kind of events in common and all make the assumption that we will experience the Awaking in two distinct phases, this may not necessarily be the case."

"Well, first of all, what are the phases?" I asked.

"As the predictions all would have it, the first phase would involve death and destruction on a massive scale and would last for some years. The second phase they describe as being a sustained period of peace, harmony and tranquility such as humans have never before experienced.

"We up here, of course, know this to be the 'heaven-on-earth syndrome.' Right Jack?"

I nodded my agreement. I was feeling really nervous. Harley wouldn't be telling me all this if it weren't really pertinent to my mission, but it was beyond me to see how I might make any kind of impact on it. Harley continued.

"Up to now humans have interpreted the writings to mean that they would experience extreme conditions first and then, having paid their spiritual dues so to speak, would get to experience the bliss and joy on the back end.

"This fits well with their belief in the no pain, no gain theory. It is also analogous to the concept of a healing crisis. This occurs when an organism, in overcoming a sickness, experiences a dramatic worsening of the situation just prior to making a dramatic shift in the direction of healing."

"Don't we see that a lot in humans when their conditions of life get so unbearable that they go through their dark night of the soul and then awaken?" I interjected again. "Isn't that the same as a healing crisis, Harley?"

"Quite right, Jack." replied Harley. "And that might well be the choice that the souls incarnate at that 'now' might make. The masses may offer so much resistance to awakening and stay so completely stuck in the three dimensional view of reality, that there will be no other option than for those who know the truth and can create effects in the world, to manifest the very kind of massive cataclysmic events of which the prophets have foretold.

"If it happens that way, so be it. But the point is, Jack, that it need not happen that way — and this is where you may have a role to play. You may be able to show humanity that there really is another way to come to this awakening transformation and that it can be easy. However, you must also convince them of the fact that the time is NOW.

"What our dear soul brother and lightworker, Gregg Braden, is trying to show the human race through his spiritual writings is what the prophets were actually seeing were alternate realities that, through the complexities of time warps, were becoming available simultaneously. It was as if two ribbons of reality were suddenly floating so close together that everyone could make an instantaneous leap from the one to the other.

"What this means, Jack, is that the human race has arrived at a point of choice whether to have the kind of future that involves massive dislocation, pain and death OR one that offers immediate peace, LOVE and tranquility. ***The choice is to awaken and be present in the Heaven on Earth scenario or perish in the process of resisting it.***

"Your job will be to give people the awareness of what the choice is and then to provide them with the spiritual technology to make the choice explicate. We have those technologies, Jack, so that part is taken care of. What you will have to do is provide the leadership such that they fully understand the choice and follow your lead in making the right choice."

"Harley, I am blown away by all this. How am I to do all this? This is a huge assignment! In a way, I feel that my backside is really on the line here. Here we are at the most important nodal point in the expansion plan of Universal Intelligence and the responsibility is all on me to have it turn out to be either the most massive cataclysmic event in the entire history of the Earth involving the annihilation of three quarters of the human race and all that it has ever created in physical form, or the most peaceful and blissful transition to heaven on earth! No pressure there, eh Harley?"

Harley, looked at me long and hard. "You're right, Jack. Your ass is on the line. But I know you can handle it. In the meantime, get some more rest. Tomorrow I will outline the direction that your actual life will take. I will show you who your parents will be, what your life will be like up until the very moment when you will be called to rise to the occasion. I think you will find it interesting."

With that he was gone.

18: Enter Eric/Shadeem

I was there early waiting for Harley. I had hardly slept a wink wondering what this incarnation was going to be like. I was really feeling the weight of the awesome responsibility that I was going to have to carry.

Even that might be OK if, when I got down there I had some awareness of it. What scares the pants off me is the idea that I won't know. I will just think I am like everyone else and have only my own little life to lead. Beyond carving out a decent sort of life-style for myself, procreating and doing something meaningful with my life in the way of productive work, I might not ever imagine that there could be any more to it than that. Suppose I become an alcoholic, for example, and completely screw up my life, or become a drug addict, or a monk even. Anything might happen to prevent me from fulfilling that mission.

During my sleep I had a nightmare. I saw myself coming home expecting a joyous homecoming, only to behold a sea of soul faces full of the deepest disappointment — all looking at me. "What's the matter?" I asked them. "You look terrible."

"There will be no heaven on earth for a very long time, Jack. You didn't awaken. You became the powerful person you were supposed to become and you had the power to make the change but you didn't wake up. You didn't hear your Higher Self screaming at you on the inside trying to get you to wake up and do what you went in to do. You became so focussed on money, status, fame and personal power that nothing else could get your attention. You blew it, Jack! Thanks a lot!"

Suddenly it hit me. All my lessons with Harley and Jeni came flooding back into my consciousness along with every detail of my mission — at this point so mindlessly unfulfilled. No heaven on earth for UI just because I failed to set the alarm correctly and didn't wake up! If I were human I would simply pray to die, but even that isn't an option in this world. Nevertheless, I still wanted to. I felt terrible. Mercifully, I woke up at that point but I was feeling awful.

Harley appeared and as usual saw right into me. "Don't worry Jack, you will have a lot of help when you go down there. You will have your own two personal life guides of course, the Ego and the Higher Self, as well as a whole bunch of independent guides plus more angels than you can imagine helping you in this mission. Then there's all the other souls incarnating with you. They have all their guides and angels in tow as well, so you will not be alone. You're just going to have to trust the process and keep in mind, there is no such thing as failure. Whatever happens is what is meant to be."

"I know, Harley, " I said. "But it's been hard. I just wanted an ordinary incarnation with ordinary lessons to learn. I was ready for betrayals, abandonments, messy divorces and financial ruin just like most of the others. I felt that I would be able to handle those kinds of things and come back ready to appreciate fully the Oneness and unconditional LOVE that exists in truth. But this assignment is of another order entirely and frankly I am scared. But then again, I know you're right. I cannot, in reality, screw up and I will have tremendous support, I know that. Who's this, Harley?"

I had suddenly become aware of the fact that someone else had entered the room with Harley. Respectfully, he had kept his distance while Harley and I were having our intimate exchange, but now he came forward and took my hand.

"Hello, Jack. I'm Eric. It seems that I am to be your partner — actually your adversary to be more precise. Not his nemesis though, right Harley?"

"That's right," said Harley, waving his hand indicating for us to be seated. "Jack, I mentioned earlier that you would be partnering with another soul who would play out the necessary dramas with you to enable the mission to be accomplished. That is quite normal of course. That is how almost every incarnation is arranged—not just with partners either. Whole soul groups might be involved. You will meet the other members of your soul group later but I wanted you to meet Eric now and for you both to be present while I outline how each of your lives will unfold and eventually intertwine.

"I have told Eric most of what he needs to know about you and where you are in your development, but since Eric has only just been assigned to the mission, I haven't until now had the chance to tell you about him. So, I will do that before we get started. Hope you don't mind, Eric?"

"Not in the least," replied Eric without the least hesitation and leaning back casually in his chair.

He had an air of confidence and knowingness about him that was reassuring but at the same time not exactly endearing. Even though my vibration was now becoming extremely close to the human frequency, I did resist the temptation to make assessments of Eric based on my perceptions. I would wait and see.

"Good," said Harley. "No need to say much anyway—just enough for you both to feel satisfied that there is a good match here and that you know what resources the other brings to the table. As I said, Eric already knows yours."

Harley then read out all Eric's special knowledge and expertise and I was suitably impressed. He had been connected with many very high powered incarnations most of which Harley had been in control. That meant Harley had a lot of confidence in him and knew him to have a huge capacity for LOVE. That meant he could endure a great deal of negative energy being projected onto him while in a human body, because he could immediately transmute it to LOVE.

For Harley that was always the major requirement for anyone whose mission required that they appear to be evil in the extreme. That gave me some comfort at least. I reasoned that if he had been picked to play the 'bad' one this time, I might basically be playing the 'goodie.' However, I did recall Harley saying that he had seen the LOVE capacity in me too, so maybe there might be some swing in fortune between us in that regard. Nevertheless, I did feel that Eric had the edge on me in the LOVE department and, though it might have been wishful thinking, I did conclude that he was more likely than I to play the heavy.

"OK, that takes care of the formalities," said Harley. "Any questions, Jack?" Harley put the question in a way that made me feel he didn't want me to ask Eric anything further. He clearly wanted to get down to business.

"No, at least not for the moment," I responded, still feeling very uncomfortable. "Maybe later."

"Good," said Harley. "Let's get right down to business. We don't have a lot of 'now' left to play with, Jack."

19: My Parents

Recognizing that time was becoming of the essence from the standpoint of my vibrational rate, Harley began to speak hurriedly.

"Since you have already received the energetic imprint for becoming human, your vibration is really changing quickly. We don't usually take this long to prepare a soul for the journey, but we've had several disruptions and changes of plan since we first started working with you. I don't want you to start taking on physical form before you've gone through the portal. That would not be good.

"Not only that, things are really hotting up down there so you really need to get going so that you are in the right place at the right time—just when you are needed. On that plane, timing is everything."

"You're right Harley, I am feeling stuff. It's like I can almost feel a body around me. It's very weird. Can't you slow the process down a bit?" I asked.

"No need," replied Harley. "We've got it handled, don't worry. Let's get on.

"You may be pleased to know that we have selected your parents already. Usually, the incarnating soul is involved in that choice but since this is a special assignment, Jack, we've had to take executive action on this occasion. Sorry about that, but that's how it is.

"Anyway, I don't think you'll be disappointed. You have a set of parents with a lot of baggage that they'll hand on to you right off the bat to deal with, but nothing you cannot handle. Oh, you will go a bit wild and take up drugs and alcohol for a while, especially during your teens and early adulthood but nothing really serious. You'll work through most of the generational baggage, except that which we want you to save for when you are called upon."

"You mean, I might know when I am called upon?" I asked hopefully.

"Absolutely not!" he replied very quickly and sharply. "But you will be given a lot of signs and signals from your Higher Self and all the other souls around you."

"Your parents will be extremely rich and powerful people, especially your father. This family has been in the energy business for a long time — I don't mean our kind of energy — I mean fuel. Fuel is what humans have to use to make the physical world work. They put it in machines and then set light to it. I am not really very well up on those kinds of things, but I do know that when they put it in airplanes and cars and burn it, the planes and cars move around quite quickly. It's not like here where all we have to do is think where we want to be next and *poof*—there we are. Because they are so dense and heavy, humans have to invent all sorts ways to overcome gravity. It's really quite a problem for them.

"Of course, one person's problem is another's opportunity. People like your father have made great fortunes supplying that stuff that people want to put in cars and airplanes to make them go fast.

"Anyway, that's the kind of business your father was involved in, at least until more important things came along for him to do.

"But more importantly, Jack, he is a person who has wielded and continues to wield, enormous power and influence. He has held very high office in the American government—and that's going to work very well for you, at least down the road. It's going to put you just where you'll want to be to fulfill that mission of yours.

"In the beginning though, it will present you with some problems growing up. Being a rich kid can have its problems, I understand, but being the son of..."

"Oh, so I definitely am going to be a male then?" I interrupted. That distinction hadn't been made up to now.

"Oh, yes," replied Harley. "You will be born a boy and you will be the eldest of two boys born to these parents. And by the way, one member of your soul group will be that brother. We are not quite certain which one at this moment, but it won't matter all that much. He will play a role in your mission, that much is certain, but it won't be so big that we have to choose someone with the amount of LOVE that, for instance, you will need. He will be a good support for you though.

"Now, where was I? Oh yes, being a son of a rich and powerful father — yes, it can be tough on a boy growing up, especially in the teenage years.

"Having a famous father makes you special in the eyes of everyone else and they will have high expectations of you. If you don't measure up it can be hard and people will judge you severely. Others, of course, will resent you and do everything they can to tear you down.

"This is exactly what you will be experiencing in those early years, Jack. You will feel inadequate and not quite good enough to get the complete approval of your father. He is not an emotional man by any means and you will feel strongly that he is not emotionally available to you. You will feel isolated and insecure around him. You will always be seeking his approval and yet always feeling that you will never get it.

"These will be some of the early lessons we have set up for you, Jack. You will not be blessed with a great deal of intelligence. No, wait. Let me say that differently. We have blessed you by ***not*** making you very smart.

This is because your mission is going to require someone who is very simplistic in their thinking; someone who sees everything as being either this or that—black vs. white, good vs. evil, so to speak; hardly able to comprehend the grey areas that might lie in between."

"I don't much like that idea, Harley," I said with considerable chagrin. "You give me all that responsibility and then deny me the brains to carry it out. What's that about?"

"Jack, it's good that you will not be all that smart. It will force you to depend on other higher order capabilities—intuition for example. You will develop a lot of that through your turbulent and far from illustrious early years—mainly as a survival technique. Family connections and money will help a lot, but there's no doubt that your intuition will get you out of a whole lot of embarrassing situations that otherwise could put you in jail.

"You are going to have to rely on your gut a great deal in this mission Jack. That means listening to your intuition and inner guidance—much more important than intelligence—at least as far as this mission is concerned."

"What mission, Harley?" I cried in exasperation feeling that Harley was just spinning it out because he didn't really want to tell me what it was. "Please tell me how I am going to heal America and create Heaven on Earth."

"Be patient, Jack. I'm coming to it," he replied with a sideways glance at Eric.

I realized in that moment that Eric had already been briefed. He already knew what the mission was. I didn't like that one little bit, but decided to say nothing.

20: The Plan Unfolds

Harley picked up on my discomfort with Eric but I imagine he just put it down to my becoming more and more humanlike in my behavior. "OK," he went on. "I see that you're wanting me to cut to the chase here, Jack, so I'll spare you all the gory details of how the early part of your life will unfold. Suffice it to say that it won't be anything anyone would be really proud of. Nevertheless, it will all be in Divine Order because you will get the lessons from it that you will need later on. It will help you develop all the right character traits and aspects of personality that you will need to carry out your mission."

"Can you give me some examples?" I enquired. Vanity and false pride were beginning to enter into my consciousness already—human qualities, no doubt. I found myself wanting those traits to be good ones, not negative. I wanted to be liked—even adored—if I was going to be famous like my father.

"Well, we've already mentioned that you are going to be very simplistic in your thinking—and, in spite of your own very questionable moral background, become very moralistic and righteous. You will also be very controlling and dictatorial—even ruthless—especially towards people you see as a threat to your power. You will be very sensitive to criticism and at times even a little paranoiac. That will tend to make you very reactive and petulant and you will always have a tendency to want to severely crush anyone who wants to criticize you—all of which is just perfect for your career in state and local politics!"

"So I am going to follow in my father's footsteps then," I said. "What political office will I hold?"

"You will be in the Oklahoma State Legislature for a while and then, later on just like your father, you will be elected to the United States Senate. You will do only a mediocre job as a Senator but, in spite of that, something will drive you to seek the nomination to become President of the United States. All the pundits will snigger and write you off but they won't know that we'll be pulling the strings up here to make that happen and that it's all part of the plan.

"You, of course, will have no awareness of this either and you will feel somewhat swept along by events. It will be hard for you—and even harder for those that handle you—to understand why you seem to do so well in the polls no matter how inarticulate your speeches are, how many gaffs you make and how silly you look on television with that irritating twitch in the corner of your mouth we're going to give you—the one that will show up when you try to smile but don't really mean it or have just told a lie."

"Oh, Come on, Harley!" I exclaimed, "Do you have to do that kind of thing? Why do you want to humiliate me? It's bad enough that you make me appear stupid — I'll be ridiculed for that — now you want me to have some kind of facial tick? You know how Americans are about their looks, Harley!"

"Ummmm — seems you've picked up the sensitivity to criticism already Jack."

"You bet I have, Harley," I rejoined. "And I can tell you it doesn't feel good!"

"That's wonderful — just what we want," Harley shot back. "You see, Jack, we want you to be humiliated and criticized — to keep you perturbated the whole while, just like you are now. I know it doesn't seem like it, but it's all going to count in the end. I know it's hard, especially now that you are starting to feel like a human being already, but try to leave the details to us and rest assured that what we are setting up here is perfect in every sense."

"OK." I reluctantly agreed, glancing towards Eric who was sitting there with a supercilious grin on his face, looking all superior. He actually winked at me!

"So, what's his role in this?" I said, making a dismissive sort of gesture in the direction of Eric but without taking my eyes off of Harley. "Is he going to be my opponent in the Presidential race, or my running mate who will eventually betray me, or what?"

"No, nothing like that," replied Harley. "Let me tell you about Eric. He will be born to the two parents we have selected for him who are wealthy merchants in a country located in the area of the planet that the humans call the Middle East. The fact that this is the area of the Earth where that fuel stuff comes from is something you should bear in mind—because as you will recall, your father made his fortune by drilling for and selling that stuff. It's going to be a crucial factor in the drama that we are creating here.

"Like everyone else in that country Eric's parents are Muslims. He will be born with the name Shadeem and will be the second eldest of four children, three of them boys.

"Whereas your upbringing will be relatively easy and you will be given all you want—with the exception of your father's approval perhaps—Shadeem's early life will be harsh and extremely difficult. His father, a cruel and sadistic man, will beat him unmercifully virtually every day of his young life and his mother will not be able to protect him. She will even betray him by always telling his father about something Shadeem will do that day, knowing that he will be beaten and shut away for hours in a dark room as a consequence. One of his younger brothers is favored by the father so, in order to keep his father's approval, he, too, will continually betray Shadeem.

"In short, Jack, by the time Shadeem reaches adulthood he will have been thoroughly brutalized. He will be full of rage and obsessed with the idea of gaining power over everyone so he can control his environment so that no one can hurt him any more."

Harley noticed me cast another glance over at Eric. I was already beginning to soften my attitude towards him now that I know what he was volunteering for.

"Eric knows all this, Jack, said Harley. "He knows just how hard this will be and he's certain that he can handle it. Right, Eric?"

"Piece of cake," replied Eric.

"Not that easy, my friend," cautioned Harley before turning his attention to me. "Anyway, all that will be in preparation for what he has to do to support your mission, Jack.

"Shadeem's father has influence and will get Shadeem into the army on a good career track. He'll get promoted quickly and often. As an officer, Shadeem will be both ruthless and cunning. He will demand total loyalty from those under him and will continually plot and scheme to undermine those above him so that they are removed to make way for him.

"Within 10 years he will have become a general in the most elite part of the army and shortly thereafter will stage a coup which will topple the government. He will then become the Head of State.

"At the time that happens, you will still be doing your dilettante stuff and just 'dicking around' at the edges of politics and business, still feeling isolated from your father and still trying—and failing —to get your father's approval.

"By the way, Jack, that's one of the threads that will bind you and Shadeem together. Both you and he will feel deprived of your father's approval and each of you will seek desperately to find it in some sublimated form all through your lives.

"Ironically, there will come a time when Shadeem actually tries to kill your father. That turns about to be one of the things that will trigger a whole chain of events that will transform the world,—but I am jumping ahead here. We'll get to that later.

"Anyway, in the intervening years while you are still fumbling your way through all sorts of projects and business dealings and playing at being a United States senator, Shadeem will really consolidate his power over his country and become its sole and undisputed dictator.

"Anyone who disputes that will be quickly executed, even if it is a family member. By the way, he will have his brother—the one who betrayed him—tortured and killed as soon as he becomes Head of State, serving as a clear warning to anyone else who might be disloyal to him.

"Like other dictators before him, he will become excessively cruel and sadistic—taking personal pleasure in watching people being tortured just like his father tortured him— and participating in the executions of anyone who he thinks might have betrayed him.

"He will also torture and kill anyone who he feels is criticizing him — another trait you two will have in common, Jack — and will use weapons of great terror to suppress any sign of rebellion within the country. He will go on to commit genocide on thousands of his own people because they are wanting some independence. Not a nice guy!

"He will also be much given to self-glorification. He'll build statues of himself and erect huge posters everywhere depicting his image. He'll spend an incredible amount of the country's money building countless palaces — all to compensate for his feelings of inferiority instilled in him by his father, of course. But no matter how many palaces he builds, it will never be enough. He'll never feel enough. He'll crave acceptance but sublimate it through the cruel exercise of power. Not being able to get people to love him, he will at least get people to be loyal to him — through fear.

"At one point he will go to war with his neighboring country and uses weapons of terror on them too, but since the United States doesn't much like that country, the US will turn a blind eye. They will even sell him weapons and do all it can to help him win that war."

21: Showdown

It was now obvious why I had already developed a strong dislike for Eric even before we had incarnated. Clearly I was going to find myself obsessed with this dictator once I got to the Earth plane. Even though Eric had not yet become Shadeem, that energy pattern had already begun to form.

"Now, here's where it starts to get really interesting," continued Harley. "Just after your father becomes appointed as US Secretary of State—interestingly enough by Glenda Shapiro, the first woman President to hold that office—Shadeem decides to invade another neighboring country, with the intention of gaining total control over that stuff we were talking about earlier that made your father so rich —I think it's called oil—that people down there value so much.

"He goes in thinking that America will turn a blind eye like last time, but this time your Dad goes ballistic. He can see his own fortune and the wealth of the U.S., being threatened by this unstable brutish dictator who wants to control the world's supply of that oil stuff and he isn't going to allow it.

"As it happens the President isn't very interested in foreign affairs and she tends to delegate a great deal of that to her Secretary of State. That is after all, his job as I understand it and she trusts him implicitly. He persuades her that the U.S. should go to war against Shadeem and to use the military might of the U.S. to get him out. So, with the support of Congress, she agrees to go to war against Shadeem."

"Harley, I notice in your languaging you are sometimes talking in the past tense and at other in the present or future tense. Can you give be a reason for that?" I asked.

"Yes, of course. Not so much a reason though as a justification. We don't normally have a past/future orientation up here, you know that. However, for the purpose of explaining your mission — which happens in time — I am having to describe things all at the same time as if they are happening 'now,' will happen or have happened already. Some of what I am describing as having happened is in fact what will happen when you incarnate, so in reality it hasn't happened yet.

"It does seem a little confusing, but don't worry about it. When you get into the World of Humanity everything will happen in the right chronological order, you will be born on the right date, in perfect synchronization with all the other people you will be doing this dance with. It will all work out the way it is supposed to. What we are doing here is giving you enough of the background so that when you do awaken, the knowledge will be there. Does that help?"

"Yes, it helps a lot. Thank you." I replied. I was very appreciative of Harley's patience with me.

"Anyway, America wins the war very decisively, of course, humiliating Shadeem in the process. It was a rout but having pushed Shadeem's army out of the other country, America decides not to kill Shadeem but to leave him in power.

"We had to play a strong hand in that situation from up here, Jack. We made the President decide to stop the war before anyone killed Shadeem and she took a lot of flak for that. But we had to prevent Shadeem's death at all costs for the sake of the mission. This was only the warm-up phase to prepare for when you would come along to bring the whole thing to fruition. If your dad had killed Shadeem — and believe me, he would have loved to do it — it would have ruined the mission. Your Dad never forgave the President for not letting him finish the job.

"When Shadeem invaded that country he had done so thinking that his old friend America would support him or at the very least not oppose him. When Glenda Shapiro actually declared war against him, he saw it, of course, as the ultimate betrayal. It was a replay of his childhood drama where his mother betrayed him by leaving him to the mercy of his father.

"Nevertheless, he knew the President well enough to know that she wouldn't have considered war as a possibility. She would have tried negotiating with him and may have demanded his withdrawal, but she never would have declared war. No, your father was the one who pushed it to that extreme.

"He forced the President's hand into making war on Shadeem and that made your dad a marked man in Shadeem's eyes — he wanted him killed for betraying him so badly. You can see how that might have worked, can't you, Jack?"

"Yes, I can." I replied "It is pretty clear to me now that Shadeem is playing out all his unresolved childhood issues around his mother and father and using the President and my father-to-be to do it. What a perfect set up!"

"That's right, Jack," agreed Harley. "Shadeem was playing out his unresolved issues with his mother and father, and acting out his intense rage. Interestingly enough there is on the Earth Plane at this 'now,' a spiritual technology called Radical Forgiveness that might have helped Shadeem forgive his parents and shift his consciousness in such a way that the war might not have had to occur at all.

"Meanwhile of course, no one has realized the fact that Shadeem was providing an opportunity to heal America's shadow, so it fell to a dictator in the Balkans to try something similar for a while. This was still while Glenda Shapiro was President, but by then your father had been fired and she had appointed a new Secretary of State.

"This dictator in the Balkans was another of our big guns — all part of the overall plan, by the way, Jack. He's still down there 'now,' standing trial for war crimes, otherwise I'd introduce him to you. His soul name is Victor. When you create the conditions for Heaven on Earth to come, Jack, we'll get together all the souls who had key roles in the transformation and have a great party.

"Anyway, as a cruel dictator he was very big on ethnic cleansing. He pushed millions of people out of their home country and made them walk hundreds of miles to another country as the whole world watched on their TV sets.

"It really pushed buttons in America because it resonated the shadow stuff on the Native American Indian issue. In particular it evoked the Trail of Tears, a shameful event where thousands of Cherokee Indians were rounded up and marched two thousand miles to some barren ground in Oklahoma that no one else wanted, so that white farmers could have their land.

"But America did the typical projection thing—vilified this leader as embodying the face of Evil and then bombed the hell out of his country. We have never seen America so self-righteous—a sure sign that they were projecting and an indication that Victor had come close to healing that shadow piece.

"But again, it didn't happen. America put that out of its mind and forgot all about it, focussing its attention instead on buying vehicles called SUV's. In other words, the American people went back to sleep.

"None of this happens on your watch, Jack, but you will come on the scene shortly afterwards. You will have been in the White House for a period of only four months when the next wake up call occurs.

"We'll take a short break and then I will quickly explain an aspect of the Radical Forgiveness technology to you that I mentioned might have stopped the other war. I know you're anxious for me to fill you in about how your election goes and everything, but it is important that you learn about this part of the technology because you will be called upon to use it at a critical time in your mission."

22: Mirrors

Harley didn't have time to explain all there was to know about the technology he referred to as Radical For giveness. However, he did feel it necessary to remind me of that part of it I had learned from Jeni about the concept of mirroring. That way, I could see how it would apply in this scenario.

"You will recall from your earlier lesson," Harley began, "that the most powerful way to clear unconscious repressed material from your shadow is to attract, through the Law of Attraction, people into your life who have the very same qualities in them that you hate in yourself.

"The principle is, *'if you spot it, you've got it!'* The degree to which that quality you see in this person or people upsets you represents the extent to which you cannot stand that quality about yourself—even though you may have no idea what it might be. The trick is to realize that this person is mirroring that quality for you and is therefore giving you a chance to love and accept it in yourself.

"This is where that Radical Forgiveness technology comes in, Jack. It provides some very simple tools to help bring this all to your awareness and then, in a very simple, easy and subtle way, connects you with the TRUTH of who you are—which is, of course, LOVE. In the instant that this occurs your shadow is immediately cleared of this repressed material. After that you won't attract that kind of person into your life again—or if you do, it simply won't affect you.

"It is a very advanced spiritual technology and is healing many people on the planet even at this 'now.' It is in fact, going to play an extremely big role in your mission, Jack. Millions of people will follow your example and use it to awaken. You will be introduced to it at a crucial moment in your life and you will learn all that you have to learn about it at that time. Suffice it for 'now' that you understand how the mirroring aspect of it will affect how the drama between you and Shadeem will play out.*

"Do you recall when I revealed your mission to you that I said it was to heal the fractured soul of America?"

"I certainly do!" I replied. "How could I forget? I am still waiting to see how I might do something so grandiose. Is this Radical Forgiveness technology the key, Harley?"

"As a matter of fact, it is." Harley replied. It will be through Radical Forgiveness and other spiritual technologies that, like Radical Forgiveness, connect the people of the world to the

---

For the basic underlying assumptions of Radical Forgiveness, see Appendix I.

TRUTH of who they are and return them to LOVE, that Heaven on Earth will become a reality.

"Remember, the idea behind this mirroring principle is that people — or countries — only get upset when someone resonates in them what they detest in themselves and have denied, repressed and projected onto the other person or country. Bear in mind, Jack, that a country has a group psyche and a soul of its own, just like a person. It also has a group shadow with all sorts of repressed trauma and generational pain held there — all of which is toxic to the country's soul. Just like many other countries, America has a soul that is fractured and in desperate need of healing."

"So, let me see if I am reading this correctly, Harley," I ventured. "I am assuming that a country like America will do the same thing as a person. It will attract to itself another country to mirror its shadow in order to heal its soul. Correct?"

Harley nodded. "Because humans are so asleep," he went on, "the leaders of the country don't recognize this as a healing opportunity, so they demonize the country they have attracted for the purpose of healing and treat it as an enemy. If they go to war with that country and beat them, then they will simply find someone else to project the country's shadow onto — and so it goes on."

"So what I think you are saying," I continued, "is that Shadeem has volunteered to mirror America's shadow thereby providing another terrific opportunity for America to heal? Is that the case?"

"Exactly," said Harley. "That is what all relationships do. You learned that in your lesson with Jeni. Why would this one be different?"

"Well, in this case we have a country on the one side and a person on the other," I replied. "Shadeem may be a Head of State, but it is he and what he does as a person that upsets everyone. America is not upset with his country—just with him. Can an individual like that heal a whole country like America?"

"Absolutely," Harley responded. "It doesn't make any difference who or what is doing the mirroring or being projected upon. The principle is the same."

"So, what America hates in Shadeem is simply a reflection of the contents of America's shadow. Right?" I asked.

"That's correct," said Harley. "And what's more the collective consciousness of America, which yearns to heal and move on from it's painful past, has created Shadeem precisely for this purpose. America has deep wounds which it hasn't been able to heal on its own. It needs someone like Shadeem to help it heal and in the end, Jack, it's going to take you to finally make that happen."

"You mean, America has so much resistance to the idea that the enemy is not the enemy at all—and that the real enemy is the enemy within, that the people won't see it unless someone in a position of power takes the lead on it?"

"Exactly," replied Harley. "And we have set it up so it will fall to you to do it when you become President."

"Oh, so I am going to be elected after all, am I," I said somewhat sarcastically. "In spite of the twitch?"

Harley grinned, but waited. Though I was being facetious in my comment, the import of the words Harley had just uttered was not lost on me. I was going to have to take the lead in teaching the nation that our enemies are our teachers and are offering us a chance to heal our collective soul.

"I hear you Harley, I said, "But even from up here that looks like a hard sell. One of the reasons there are so many millions of Americans incarcerated there — more than all other nations combined—is that senators and congressmen get elected by being tough on crime. No one ever got elected by being pro-criminal! It's hard to imagine *'love your enemies and forgive the convicts for they only reflect our consciousness,'* playing well in the primaries!

"It's also pretty hard to imagine how a President like me with only half a brain and a twitch would be able to convince the Congress that this isn't a half-crazed notion proposed by someone who ought to be locked away in a mental institution!"

"It's not going to happen like that, Jack," said Harley, reassuringly. "You're right, though. You'll never convince anyone of this through argument and reason. No, it will come about through an energetic realignment in the overall field of consciousness shared by all who live in America.

"But, just as in the same way that, if America shifts, other countries will likely follow suit because everyone will be drawn to where the power is centered, the American people will follow its President if the lead is clear enough.

"The lead you will give, Jack, will manifest not through words — which is why we have made you as inarticulate as we dared, lest you should try — but through the light that will shine from you when your consciousness shifts. You will become a beacon of light and the American people will respond to that. You'll see."

23: Hot Buttons

Though my general understanding of how mirroring might work to heal America through its inter actions with Shadeem, I still wanted Harley to come up with some specifics.

"Just for the record, Harley, at least give me some idea of what Shadeem is reflecting in the American collective shadow," I suggested. "What is it that he does that pushes our buttons so badly?"

[Notice the 'our' — seems I'm already an American even before I get a body — literally an 'out-of-body American!'].

"All right," said Harley. "I have been doing some research on that because I knew that you would want to know. I have been asking all the recently returned ex-American souls what they thought and I have come up with the following list. It is not exhaustive, but it will give you the idea, I think.

"Number one on the list of things that Americans get upset about is the fact that he has committed genocide on his own people and his neighbors, dropping weapons of mass terror on innocent people."

"OK," I said. "So what might that be resonating in the American psyche?"

"Well, I am told that the genocide of the native American Indians went on for a more than a century," replied Harley. "There is a more or less direct correlation there. I believe Jeni mentioned this to you in your lesson on generational pain. Then there were all the arbitrary lynchings and killings of blacks that went on for decades even after emancipation, killings that went virtually unpunished. The Government of the United States actually carried out experiments on black prisoners, without their knowledge or permission, exposing them to differing levels of radiation just to see what the effects might be. The Americans also used a weapon of mass destruction in Hiroshima and Nagasaki, killing many thousands of people in a single stroke."

"OK, I can see that Shadeem's use of genocide and weapons of mass destruction on his own people and his enemies pushes America's buttons over their repressed shame about their own record in this area, but what other things did you find out?" I asked.

"Well, Americans see Shadeem as a cruel dictator with no regard for people's freedom or human rights," replied Harley.

"Is there a correlation here?" I asked. I was feeling an intense need to grasp this whole idea of how Shadeem was resonating America's shadow. It felt like it was the key to everything. What a bummer that I wouldn't remember it though!

"Clearly, America's own dismal record of human rights is being resonated here, especially the cruelty involved in its one hundred years of institutionalized slavery of black people. Add in another 100 years of Jim Crow laws under which blacks were subjected to sub-human treatment in the extreme and for which no official apology has ever been made, plus the discrimination against black people that continues to the present 'now' and you can quite readily see how their buttons get pushed on this issue—big time."

"What about the fact that he incarcerates people and summarily executes his enemies without trial?" I asked. "How does that resonate with America's shadow material"

"America has more people incarcerated as a proportion of its population than any other country in the world. Its prison population exceeds the number of all other prisoners in the world combined. America is proud of its justice system but deep down it knows that it is thoroughly corrupted by money, politics and racial prejudice. Most prisoners are black and/or too poor to be able to afford a good defense lawyer so they get poor justice. Most of them are in prison for reasons that have nothing to do with crime, but for moral and political reasons such as for smoking marijuana. America is the only civilized country in the world to retain the death penalty and the people on death row are almost always poor, black and not infrequently innocent. They get convicted because the system fails them. Everyone knows the justice system is badly flawed and is money driven, but no-one wants to look at it, because America proclaims that it stands for freedom."

"Wow! I bet that all weighs really heavy on their soul," I mused. "To be the beacon of freedom, equality and justice in the world and yet have to carry that burden must be awful for them. I feel so much compassion for the people of America at this 'now.' What else, Harley?"

"Well," replied Harley, "It is interesting that America gets very upset about the fact that Shadeem cannot be trusted and reneges on all his agreements. Yet America broke every treaty it ever made with the Native American Indian whenever it suited its purpose to do so. America accuses Shadeem of playing games, but that's exactly what they did with the Indians, time and time again. That must weigh heavily on their soul, too."

"And didn't the President of America incite Shadeem's own people to rebel against Shadeem on the understanding that America would help, and then walked away leaving them to be slaughtered?" I added.

"That's right," said Harley. "There's plenty more, but that's enough to illustrate the point. Everything that they find unacceptable about Shadeem is lurking in the American shadow, just waiting to be integrated and healed. Shadeem is simply their mirror."

"But is America any different to any other country in that regard, Harley?"

"Of course not," said Harley emphatically. "Great Britain, for example, has plenty of shadow stuff to deal with—probably more than America if only because it has been going on for so long. It's colonial history alone is probably enough to match America's past. Don't forget too, that it was Great Britain who occupied Iraq in 1917 and arbitrarily carved out its present boundaries. No, America is no different. In fact it probably has the least shadow material of any other major country in the world—on a par with Australia I would say. Both are young countries which means they haven't had too much time to amass a deep shadow.

"But one of the main reasons why America's shadow is not as deep as some countries is that the founding fathers of that country were Divinely guided in creating their constitution. That document and the Bill of Rights have been the touchstones for all Americans and have really helped to keep the whole country on a good course, notwithstanding some notable deviations along the way."

"So why are you focussing on clearing America's shadow first," I enquired.

"The reason we are wanting to clear America's shadow first is that we need America to be as pure and as whole as we can get her prior to the Awakening. America has been chosen to be the perfect place where it will all begin and it will radiate out from there. So we need a healed America, a whole

America, an integrated America, a pure America. And as I said earlier, America is flexible, open and willing to shift. If she can just release the energy tied up in the past and buried in the shadow, she will fulfill her soul destiny. It has always been America's soul's destiny you know, Jack. The founding fathers knew it, of course.

"So what does it take to heal the shadow of a country, Harley?" I enquired. "What does one have to do? What will I have to do?"

"Actually, Jack, not a whole lot," replied Harley. "Just recognizing that it is there, being willing to see it, bringing it to the light, telling the truth about it, accepting it for what it is and feeling the feelings that are associated with it—that's the first major step.

"Being willing to entertain the possibility that the person we are upset with is mirroring the shadow is the next step. Then you 'radically forgive' that person *(recognizing that he or she did what he or she did not to you but FOR you),* and the shadow work is done. It really is that easy."

"That's the essence of the Radical Forgiveness technology, I presume then?" I ventured to suggest. "But can it really be that easy?"

"Yes," replied Harley. "From all that I hear from recently returned souls, Jack, this Radical Forgiveness technology is indeed both easy and very effective. And simple, too.

"What is even more interesting is that the souls are saying that the humans are now realizing that if enough people did a Radical Forgiveness worksheet on Shadeem to reach a critical mass sufficient to create a shift in consciousness, the shadow would evaporate immediately. There would then be no need for any further wars or anything like that. And it wouldn't take that many to create that critical mass. Less than 100,000 people would probably do the trick they say."

"That's incredible," I said. "After all that has happened over so much Earth time, a simple technology like that can heal it?"

"Yes," said Harley. "You will stumble on this technology at the right moment and you will use it to heal some of your own personal wounds. That's why we gave you some in your early life — so that you would experience the healing power of Radical Forgiveness. Having healed some of your wounds, you will then realize that Radical Forgiveness can be utilized to heal America's issue with Shadeem."

"What would the technology look like?' I asked. "What would one need to do?"

"One of the returning souls brought a part of it with him to show me," replied Harley. "It's basically a kind of worksheet. It doesn't look like much but apparently it is precisely its simplicity that gives it the power to move energy in a very big way. They have the same kind of thing on a CD, as well."

24: Breakdown

Picking up on where he had left off talking about how my life would actually turn out before going off on that tangent about Shadeem healing the shadow, Harley continued.

"As I recall, we were talking about your run for President and we left off with you berating me for having given you a facial tick. Well, Jack in spite of that and all the gaffs you made during the campaign, you actually become elected to the office of President of the United States. It will be by the skin of your teeth, mind you. You'll actually get fewer popular votes than the other poor guy, but you win nevertheless.

"I say 'poor guy,' because in reality if we hadn't intervened and created havoc with the voting machines in one particularly close race, he would have won. We couldn't let that happen, of course, so we went and did what we had to do to get you in. The other guy would not have suited our purpose at all. He has another mission entirely.

"I don't mind telling you though, it stretched our resources a great deal. We had to influence the minds of some really very high up dudes in the US government to get you through that mess!"

"Harley, you're talking again as if it has already happened," I complained. I am still here. I haven't incarnated yet!"

"Jack, your concern with linear time is showing again. Did I see you with a Rolex time thought form? Perhaps that's the problem. Maybe your 'now' consciousness has become polluted by this thought form. It doesn't matter whether I speak of these events as having happened or are yet to happen. It's all the same in this world.

"Anyway, once we had you in place as the President, everything started to work like clockwork — until an event occurred that rocked the United States and changed the world."

"What was that?" I asked.

"Before I tell you about that, let me back up a bit because this event is the thing that will really start the ball rolling for you and I want you to understand how we have arranged everything to align with your mission.

"Up to now you have thought of your soul group as a group of 7 or 8 souls, right? That is, after all, the normal soul group size. Well, Jack, your soul group is more than 100 times that amount and that doesn't count all the other souls not directly connected to you but who are nevertheless attached to this mission in one way or another.

"As you are well aware, the purpose of this human experience is to create painful separation in order to heighten our experience of Oneness the moment we drop the illusion of separation. Well, in order for Humanity to fully awaken so that Heaven on Earth can be created, it is necessary to bring this to a crescendo. That means creating separation—and the fear that goes with the separation—in such extreme forms that it would force a total breakdown. Out of that would come break***through.***

"But as we noted when going over and re-evaluating the underlying message behind the prophecies, while it is true that breakthrough is always preceded by breakdown, the breakdown can either be manifested in one of two ways:

a) as a total collapse of physical structures and institutions, with the breakthrough happening but slowly in the terrible aftermath of that cataclysmic collapse.

b) as the immediate creation of Heaven on Earth as a result of our acceptance of DIVINE TRUTH following an instantaneous breakdown of all existing paradigms of reality based on the illusion of separation."

"Surely we or they would choose the latter, wouldn't they, Harley? Why would humans choose the cataclysmic option?"

"Because they might leave it too late." Harley replied. "Once the breakdown really begins, it will be quick and there will be so much fear and panic that the other option won't be there any more.

"However, we are relatively optimistic. Given the state of the consciousness of the mass of the human population at this 'now,' we are, in fact, betting on a combination of these two scenarios. We feel that the way it is most likely to happen—and remember, we don't make it happen, humans have free will—is that humans will bring the world to the very brink of physical breakdown and then, at the eleventh hour, have a shift in consciousness that will result in the true breakthrough. This is where you will play a crucial role, Jack."

I was about to ask more about that, but Harley put up his hand. He was on a roll with this most crucial point and didn't want an interruption.

"Now, as I said," Harley went on, "we have to honor free will, so we cannot make it happen from up here. But we can help. We do that by sending in angels and incarnate souls who have volunteered for that mission. Obviously, that's what we are doing with you and Eric. And as you will see when Eric becomes Shadeem, he will be instrumental in creating breakdown on a big scale and actually so will you, Jack, even though of course, you will think you are doing the right thing. That's why we want you to develop that either/or simplistic self-righteous way of yours, so you will not waver in your convictions.

"Besides you and Eric, there is another who has volunteered to play a very key role and to contribute mightily to the first phase of the physical breakdown. Like you and Eric he has an enormously loving heart, otherwise he could not do this. He will be considered every bit as evil in America's eyes as

Shadeem and they will hunt him down like a dog once he successfully carries out the first part of his mission.

"His human name is Omar bin Faden. He too will be from the same part of the world as Shadeem but not the same country. His way of creating extreme separation will be to first create an extremely distorted division between the religion of Islam and Christianity. He will create what is known as a very fundamentalist version of Islam *(that in a way mirrors the fundamentalist versions of Christianity that many Americans have),* and will use that to stir up intense hatred against America.

"He will attract to him others who feel that America has become too imperialistic, greedy and concerned only with furthering its own interests throughout the world and together they will plot the destruction of America.

"They will be more than willing to give their lives to the cause and feel that if they die doing battle with 'the infidel,' they will be glorified in heaven. They even make it up that they each will be given 77 virgins to play with."

"You're kidding," I exclaimed.

"Not at all," Harley replied. "Didn't I tell you earlier that they do some pretty strange things down there in the name of their religions?

"Don't be fooled though. While it will look like madness, it is all part of the Divine plan. It will first bring America and then the rest of the world to the brink of the breakdown so that it can ultimately choose BREAK-THROUGH.

"All the people creating all this mayhem, fear and anger are members of your soul group, Jack. They are working hard to prepare the ground for you to come in and do your thing. Keep that in mind for a moment.

"What these souls do next changes everything. They plan and execute a very daring and radical plan. They simultaneously hijack two commercial airliners. They dive bomb one of them directly into a nuclear power station, causing a huge explosion and causing incredible damage to the power station. Their intent, of course, was to cause the massive release of radioactive material in order to kill millions of Americans.

"This is where we had to intervene again, Jack. There was no point in doing that much harm to people and creating so much drama. The purpose is to wake up people, not kill them in their millions. We know death is an illusion, but they don't. Remember our earlier conversation about that and how deeply in the illusion the fear of death keeps them? If we created that much mayhem, the mass consciousness would be so shattered that the likelihood of a quick transformational breakthrough happening in the wake of that would have been nil. So we neutralized the radioactivity and put a light shield around the reactor itself.

"The other plane headed towards The White House and was right on target for a direct hit, but again we intervened. Not just because you were home — we could have gotten you out in a second if we'd wanted the White House blown up — but again that kind of mayhem was not necessary. It was the symbolism that was so important. It was necessary for Americans to feel their vulnerability. Just knowing that it might easily have happened was enough.

"So we put some very brave souls on that plane who then wrestled with the so called terrorists and the plane came down in a field killing, of course, all on board.

"It was very sad for the families of all those that died in all these actions. We know that they miss their loved ones very much. It would comfort them much to know that we had a meeting with all those souls and they wished that they could let their families know that they are OK and that it was their choice to do this — for America and for humanity.

"Until this moment, Jack, America has never had to face its vulnerability. That's one of the reasons why it has never chosen to look at its shadow.

"What you will discover when you become fully human is that when you're safe and comfortable, you won't go delving into your shadow. You stay outer-directed, focussed on maintaining physical comfort and on accumulating more and more money and things. It's only when physical and emotional comfort is threatened that you begin to look inward. You begin to wonder who you really are, what drives you, what you would consider worth fighting for — even dying for. You question your values, your life-style and your relationship with others around you. You might even reconsider your relationship with God.

"That was the purpose of the terrorist incident. It made people acutely aware of their vulnerability. It might have made them a little more humble and less belligerent, but it didn't.

"It was a shake-up for them, but it didn't lead to any kind of breakdown. We didn't want that anyway. It would have been too soon and besides, you weren't ready.

"You must have realized it too, Jack, since you did such a great job selling everyone on the 'God Bless America' deal and effectively cutting off any effective conversation about the issues underlying the event. Nice job."

I was still having a hard time listening to Harley speak as if it had all happened already. It was getting harder and harder which must have meant that I was becoming more and more attached to the linear time concept in preparation for my incarnation. I couldn't resist stealing another glance of my Rolex thought form.

"Let's take another break," said Harley. When we come back, I want to focus more on how you and Eric play this whole thing out and create the BREAK***THROUGH*** for America."

25: Breakthrough

Harley reappeared but this time without Eric. It was just Harley and me again. I must say that felt better to me. There was something about Eric that made me uncomfortable even though, having learned the role he was going to have to play, I had begun to tolerate him more.

"OK, Mr. President," said Harley teasingly. "Let's see how this whole thing might play out.

"Recapping, you will be born into the Barber family—rich and highly influential oil people from Oklahoma. You are spoiled as a child, smothered by your mother and largely ignored by your father whose approval you craved then and still do.

"Your early adult life will be a mess but somehow *(with a little help from us and your soul group)* you will manage to be elected as a member of the Oklahoma Legislature and then later on to the U.S. Senate.

"You will somehow get nominated for President and you will win by a whisker — once more with a little help from your friends up here!

"Your father by this time will have retired from politics, but his nemesis, Shadeem will be still firmly in power, cocky as ever. Just before your dad retires, Shadeem tries to get him killed and comes close to succeeding. You appear incensed about that and vow to avenge that. 'No one tries to kill my dad and gets away with it,' is your attitude — the usual moralistic approach everyone has come to expect from you. *(Truth be told, you probably saw it as yet one more opportunity to win his approval).*

"The next big wake-up call comes with the terrorist event that I have already outlined. By using commercial aircraft as missiles on American soil, Omar bin Faden really gets the attention of the American people. For the first time in a very long while they get to feel vulnerable and — worse yet — unable to defend themselves. They feel unable to even identify their enemy or know what they might do next or where. The whole country goes into fear.

"You will have been in the White House for about six months when this occurs. Until then you will have been, as expected, ridiculed and lampooned by the press and all the late night comedians. One talented impersonator gets your twitch just right and regularly makes everyone fall about laughing.

"But as soon as the terrorist event happens everything changes. If ever an event made a person, this one will make you, Jack.

All of a sudden you will appear composed, in charge and decisive. Your either/or moralistic style of thinking comes in really handy because it enables you to articulate to the frightened American people what is happening in very simplistic terms. 'We are at war!' 'America is good and they are evil —God Bless America.'

"Your popularity will soar, which is of course what we want. We want the people to trust you and to follow you so that when you have your Awakening, they would follow that too.

"You go immediately to war with the country which harbors bin Faden and it will seem to go well—though I have to smile about your not being able to catch him. We're supporting him too, Jack, remember? He's as important to the mission as you and Eric are, so his role is not yet over. It's an interesting cat and mouse game seen from up here. It's funny to watch you both posturing and doing your thing, with neither one of you realizing what the truth is—that it's all an illusion.

"Oops—sorry, Jack," said Harley, "I shouldn't lapse into telling it like it is from this perspective. I ought to keep telling the story as best I can from the World of Humanity standpoint so you can see more from that perspective, but sometimes I just lose it. The whole thing is much more fun when seen from up here and it's so fascinating to see it unfolding exactly how it needs to unfold. Anyway, I'll try to behave by trying to stay more with the human drama so you will at least have a few deja-vu moments when all this stuff occurs."

"No apology required, Harley," I replied. "To tell you the truth, I prefer it when you remind me that it is all just a game and that we shouldn't worry about outcome at the human level. Universal Intelligence will get its Heaven on Earth; it's simply a question of whether the humans make it exceedingly difficult for themselves by choosing the apocalypse scenario in 2012 to attain it, or whether they decide to follow my lead by choosing the 'consciousness breakthrough 'now' scenario."

"Very good, Jack!" exclaimed Harley. "That's the first time I've heard you own that leadership role. All of a sudden it's like you are wearing it. It's part of your energy field. Wonderful!"

It was true. At last I was beginning to see exactly what my role was and I was beginning to really accept that I was worthy of the role and that I could pull it off.

I was now seeing how the life that I will be living, right from the moment I am born, will be leading me to the moment when something would occur that would awaken me from the dream of human existence and I would know who I am and understand what would need to be done to begin a mass Awakening. I would be the first President to be a spiritual leader — not in the narrow religious sense of course — but as a fully awakened human being able to bring about world peace within months rather than years and shortly thereafter — Heaven on Earth. Wow! What a privilege to be able to do this.

Suddenly, all my petty human style reservations and negative feelings I had around Eric were gone and I felt great love for him. What a loving soul he was to be willing to play the role of Shadeem, to play opposite me in creating a situation that would create the breakdown needed to have a breakthrough on a mass scale.

Then I started to have concern. What if we fail to actually create breakthrough conditions?

As usual, Harley picked up on my thoughts. "Don't worry Jack. Whatever happens will be OK. Remember, in the last analysis humans have the free will to do it however they want. If they choose not to go with our plan and we have to bring you or Eric home prematurely, that's how it will have to be.

"Indeed, it will look at times as though the plan isn't working. Even though you actually go to war against Shadeem and topple him from power, you do it too easily to create breakdown conditions. No, the war itself will not be the 'tipping point.' It is what will happen after the war that will likely cause conditions leading to breakdown, not the least of which might be the serious economic breakdown that you create by piling up enormous debt.

"So don't worry, Jack, there is plenty of potential for creating serious breakdown conditions as this whole thing continues to play itself out over a number of 'nows.' Consider too, that it is possible that you won't kill Shadeem during the war and that even after the war he will continue to play his role opposite you. He'll continue to be a thorn in your side for quite a while.

"We are also very aware that a similar scenario is evolving in North Korea so, just as we have been preparing you and Eric for this scenario, we are preparing another soul for that one. It might even work out that the two scenarios will combine, in which case you will still be involved. Same thing in Iran.

"Bear in mind too that we have had souls working through their mission in Israel and Palestine for many 'nows'—going right back to the circumstance they refer to as the Holocaust. Actually, I had a hand in steering that one," said Harley with a grin. "All these events are connected, Jack. They're all leading up to the same scenario—the Awakening, and you can be pretty sure that I will give you a strong part to play in this one too. You are going to be one busy soul down there, Jack!

"Anyway, we are satisfied that it's all gone pretty much our way so far and we do have a lot of souls down there right now trying to make things happen the right way for you. But beyond that, we simply must trust the process."

"OK, Harley," I replied, "But I am now so involved and committed now to this, I really want it to happen while I am there as President and I really want to be the one to lead the world into a new age of enlightenment."

"With that amount of intention, Jack, I believe you will. I think now is the time to take a rest. Let's meet again in a few 'nows.' We need to get this part finished and get you on your way as soon as possible.

26: Ready To Go

Harley appeared again, this time with Eric. I was pleased to see him and we melded energy fields in loving exchange. He knew how I had felt about him and was glad I had dropped all that baggage. As our energy fields came together both of us noticed the increased density and a certain degree of difficulty in actually merging, as if we each had a physical boundary.

Harley noticed of course. "We do need to speed this up. I can see that your energy fields are getting denser every moment. You will need to go through the portal or you will be too dense to make it. You could get stuck halfway, and then what?

"Picking up on the leadership issue we had finished on at the last meeting, Harley went on, "I want you to understand something about the kind of leadership role you will play.

"First of all, you will not suddenly become like some spiritual guru. You will not suddenly take to wearing flowing garments and growing a long beard. No, you will continue to look and sound presidential, but you will be different in a way no one will be able to describe.

"Your speeches will begin to take on a whole new emphasis with concepts like — brotherhood of mankind, cooperation, forgiveness, reconciliation, restitution, compassion, mutual support and sharing of resources, equality, oneness and LOVE for one another, becoming the norm.

"People will feel the difference between what you say then and how those words used to be said by you and other politicians before your Awakening. They will know that you mean them not as cliches and vote-getting code words but as guides for the way they should live in their everyday lives.

"Gone will be that false smile and that awful twitch. No more inauthentic speeches given against some rigged thematic background and reported in sound bites on the evening news. People will flock to hear you give real speeches, to experience your speaking from your heart, soul to soul.

"Through the law of attraction you will begin to have people around you who have purity of spirit, integrity, compassion and a loving heart. All the old style politicians that used to be around you will drift away and become ineffective. In the elections people with same purity of spirit will come forward and be elected.

"You will get Congress to appropriate money for mass consciousness-raising projects. For example you would quickly fund one that has already been proposed by a person who was a presidential candidate a few years ago. This proposed having at least 40,000 people at any one time, at a location in India, continually meditating for peace and transformation. That would create the critical mass required at least for world peace to occur. With proper funding, we could double that number.

"You would also get Congress to fund a worldwide Radical Forgiveness project that would dissolve the victim archetype once and for all and enable everyone to truly forgive themselves and others, drop all grievances and appearance of separation and move into oneness. That would raise the vibration of humanity to a very high level.

"You will create support only for things that improve the human condition and support the environment. You would call for a re-examination of all human values and lead people towards a way of life that leads to genuine happiness and fulfillment based on the spiritual principles of giving and receiving, infinite abundance for all, mutual support, community and so on.

"That's the kind of leadership you will create when you awaken, Jack. You will still be President—not a politician in the old sense of the word— but a true leader in the very fullest sense of that word.

"By the end of your term you will have changed the world, Jack. You will have set humanity on a new course. You will have raised the consciousness of the planet and well before 2012 created a world of forgiveness, LOVE and Harmony out of chaos, fear and despondency.

"Jack, we have brought you more or less to present time in terms of the drama being played out. You and Shadeem have work to do and it's time for you to go.

"How it plays out from this time on, we cannot tell. We have done all we can to prepare you and the situation. There is a war in preparation to be waged between you and Shadeem and right now it appears for you to be very personal. You will say many times on TV, "He tried to kill my dad." You will be accused many times of running a personal vendetta against Shadeem while others will say, it's all about oil.

"However, we know better. What people say about you and how they assess your role in the war and all that, is really irrelevant. The REAL purpose of this war — whether it occurs or not — is simply to provide another opportunity for humanity to awaken.

"Whether this war will be the event that will lead to your own Awakening, we don't know at this point, but when and if it comes we will be there for you, waiting with all the resources that you will need.

"Not since the soul of Nelson Mandela took on the mission of healing the soul of South Africa have we asked another soul to heal an entire country — especially one so powerful as the United States. And of course, never before has a soul been given the task of transforming all of humanity.

"Our blessings go with you, Jack."

Epilogue:

Happy Ever After

So there you have it. All we have to do is to wait for the President to awaken and everything will be fine.

Hey, didn't I say at the beginning that this was a spiritual fantasy—a fairy tale? Well, all fairly tales have a happy-ever-after ending and I won't be denied one.

So I am making it up here and now that, just as Harley predicted, our beloved President suddenly has a spiritual experience and leads us all into a state of nirvana and we all live happily ever after in the 4th and 5th dimension, in a state of pure bliss, harmony and LOVE.

THE END

PART FOUR

The 'In-Body' Experience

27: Down to Earth

Fairy tales, as we all know, are more than just stories. They are allegories. Within the simplicity of such stories is always a deeper meaning and a profound truth to be revealed—not in the words themselves but woven into the fabric of the story itself. Our job as the reader, or the listener, is to go beneath the words and discover the meaning and truth for ourselves and to apply it to our own lives—to experience it directly, become changed by it and act from there.

The story you have just been reading is just such an allegory. It has basically two characters—Harley, the Angel of Incarnation and Jack, the soul who receives Harley's instruction on how he will incarnate to become Jack Barber, President of the United States. It turns out that Jack Barber's soul purpose is to heal the fractured soul of America and awaken Humanity to itself.

You may have concluded fairly early on that the parallels between Jack Barber and George W. Bush were too strong to be ignored and that the likelihood was that, all along, I was alluding to 'Dubya'.

That would have been a fair assumption, but wrong nevertheless. No, the fact is that the soul whose name is Jack is none other than ***YOU.***

Harley was describing ***YOUR*** incarnation; ***YOUR*** mission. He was also describing MY incarnation and MY mission, so I am Jack too. In fact he is describing the mission of all the souls on this planet at this time—including of course, George W. Bush. ***We are ALL Jack.***

Harley was preparing all of us for the moment of Awakening; the moment when we would see the TRUTH of what is happening in the world and become willing to transform it. We don't need a President, or any kind of a leader, to do it for us. We are powerful enough to do it on our own.

So, the message of this fairy tale is that you are, at this very moment, at a point of choice. The choice is whether to awaken or go back to sleep; to live in the illusion or move into TRUTH. The choice is no less critical for you and the world than it is for George W. Bush, Osama bin Laden and Saddam Hussein. We are, after all, the same person. There is only ONE.

Now, let's suppose that your choice is to awaken. How is that going to happen? What will the Awakening feel like? Will it be a sudden rush, or will it happen gradually? How will you know that you have awakened?

We have all heard stories of how people have awakened as a result of undergoing some extraordinarily difficult ordeal. *(This is analogous to the option given in the story about how planetary awaking might have to occur through some kind of worldwide cataclysmic event that would traumatize the world and force people to awaken).*

There is no doubt that personal transformations of this kind will continue to occur for some individuals, but we now know that there is another way. We can choose it.

Because many of us already have reached a heightened awareness of the possibility that there is more to reality than we have known up to now, we are able to make the choice to go to the next step and awaken fully. This, I believe, is actually happening now to a great many people, albeit gradually and almost imperceptibly.

Over the last twenty years — since the Harmonic Convergence perhaps — awareness among the population has expanded considerably and it appears to be accelerating. Many of us have already broken free of a consciousness bounded by 5-sensory interpretation of reality. We have become 'multisensory' and aware of non-physical reality. We have found ways, such as meditation, prayer and Radical Forgiveness, to tap into what the quantum physicists refer to as the Unified Field of Consciousness, which I believe is, in fact, the World of Spirit.

This IS the process of awakening; the gradual process of becoming conscious. The very fact that you are holding this book in your hands and have got this far in the text is testimony to the fact that YOU are becoming conscious.

However, time is running out. The process needs to be accelerated even more. At this time, there is an insufficient number of conscious people on the planet to create the critical mass necessary to break us free from our limited world-view based on three dimensional reality and simple cause and effect. The prevailing mass consciousness, with its focus on materiality and its addiction to the victim archetype, continues to hurtle us in the direction of economic disaster, self annihilation and planetary destruction.

This means that we who are conscious and ready to take the lead in awakening humanity, must come together in sufficient numbers to create a powerful singularity of intention to raise the mass vibration so that the Awakening can occur.

Referencing the work of Gregg Braden, the story suggests that the Awakening can indeed take place without our having to go through a series of cataclysmic events. If that is our choice, we must begin to align with each other NOW to make that the reality.

For this to happen, we must appeal to people of every religion, race, creed and nationality in the world with a simple, universal vision of peace and a straight forward plan of action that transcends all current disagreement and grievances so that we will literally, in Harley's words create 'Heaven on Earth.'

We have the technologies to make it happen if we choose to use them. I believe that the best technology out there is Radical Forgiveness, but if you have your own favorite method of shifting your consciousness, (e.g. the Kabbalah, Transcendental Meditation, etc.), then by all means, use that.

However, it is vitally important that we do our own personal work as well. No one who is not willing to release personal grievances and emotional holdings from the past will be able to contribute to the raising of the consciousness of the planet, no matter how good their intention. How can someone who maintains a low vibration by holding onto victim consciousness, raise the consciousness of others? It is impossible. To create harmony you must be harmony; to create peace, you must be peace; to create LOVE in the world, you must be LOVE.

I urge you therefore, to make a list of all the grievances that you are holding, no matter how large or small. When you have done that, go immediately to the web site ***www.radicalforgiveness.com.*** There you will find a **FREE** Interactive Forgiveness Worksheet tutorial that will help you to literally dissolve all your grievances, one by one, and clean out your emotional closet.

You will find this tool easy to use, non-threatening and actually quite enjoyable. You will feel the energy move almost immediately and you will feel lighter for having released the energy once invested in that grievance.

If, like virtually everyone in the population it seems, you have yet to forgive your parents, there is also, on our web site, a special **21 Day Program for Forgiving Your Parents** that will enable you to do just that. There is also a two-part online **Radical SELF Forgiveness** program for deal with guilt, shame and self-hatred.

It is a fact that almost all of the life issues that we struggle with and seem to repeat over and over again, have their origins in the core negative beliefs that we formed through our childhood interactions with our parents. This is just as true for those who were blessed with 'good' parents as those whose parents truly mistreated them. The most common core negative beliefs that get repeatedly played out in everyday life, and have their beginnings in the child/parent relationship are:

> 'I'll never be good enough.'
> 'I have to be perfect to be loved.'
> 'People will always leave me.'
> 'I don't deserve to receive love.'
> 'I will never get my father's approval.'
> 'I will never get my mother's approval.'
> 'I am not worthy to receive love.'
> 'There's something basically wrong with me.'

You might recall that in the story, Shadeem had a very abusive set of parents and was beaten every day by his father and frequently betrayed by his mother. The story also portrayed Jack as always needing and not getting his father's approval. I also hinted in the story that both Jack and Shadeem were playing out their 'daddy dramas' on the world stage. Additionally, I suggested that because the President was a woman, Shadeem was acting out his 'mama drama' in creating her and setting it up so that she would betray him — just as his mother did. This is, of course, exactly how it all works.

Anyway, should you recognize any of these core negative beliefs within yourself, the best possible gift you could give yourself is to take the time to do the 21 day program. Check it out on the web site and see for yourself what it involves.

You will find in Appendix 1 of this book a brief outline of the principles and assumptions of Radical Forgiveness, but to learn more and get a deeper understanding of the Radical Forgiveness Technology and how you can apply it easily to your life, you might also wish to purchase from the web site my book, ***Radical Forgiveness, Making Room for the Miracle.***

Just reading the book and doing the tutorial on the web site will raise your vibration and enable you to practice living your life from LOVE and gentle acceptance of yourself and others while at the same time raising the consciousness of the planet.

I would emphasize the words *'at the same time,'* contained in the last sentence for I am not saying that you cannot do the planetary healing work until you have done your own personal work. That would be impossible, for who among us could ever say that we were completely free of any grievances? If we had to wait for us to be totally clean, we wouldn't even get started.

The point is that just ***making the commitment*** to work on ourselves is sufficient. Then we can, in all integrity, turn our attention to raising the consciousness of the planet as well.

We will, in fact, have gone a long way to achieving that goal when we have begun to embrace Radical Forgiveness as nothing less than a permanent way of life.

28: Fantasy vs. Science

Nothing in the story seemed so outlandishly far fetched as the notion that the President of the United States, especially the present incumbent, would awaken and lead the world in creating Heaven on Earth in his lifetime. *(No wonder I had to call this book a spiritual fantasy!)*

By the same token, not even in my wildest dreams would I have considered it possible that the government might even consider funding a major defense initiative founded on the belief that the only way to defend against terrorism is by changing our consciousness and creating world peace through meditation and spiritual practice.

It is incredible, but true, that our government has at least given consideration to a plan to use spiritual technology to diffuse all the acute ethnic, religious and political tensions in the world that fuel terrorism. Wow!

Doesn't this sound as though it could be the beginnings of what Harley was talking about and to all intents and purpose predicted? Isn't this, in fact, what we have been praying for? You must admit, it does have Harley's stamp all over it! What if Bush were to get behind such a proposal? Could it be the beginning of his Awakening?

The Rules Have Changed

Let's be realistic. If people in the government are in fact giving this idea attention at this time, it can only be because they are running scared. They know they have no real answer to the terrorist threat and that, given the new rules of the game of war which the terrorists have defined, the initiative and therefore the power are clearly with them and not with the U.S. The balance of power in the world has shifted significantly and military might is no longer any guarantee of security.

Given the new security environment then, it is not totally ridiculous to believe that top level government officials in the White House, the Department of State, Department of Defense and the National Security Council, the Army, House and Senate are reported to have taken the idea extremely seriously. A significant number of congressmen and senators have expressed support for the idea.

Backed by Good Science

Don't imagine, however, that our government has taken leave of its senses and or has gone 'wu-wu' on us. The plan being put forward has a tremendous amount of sound experimental science to back it up and is firmly rooted in the theory of quantum mechanics—just like any good spiritual technology must be, including Radical Forgiveness.

Indeed, it is the quality of the science—which has been replicated, reviewed and endorsed by many eminent scientists in many different countries around the world—that has got senators and congressmen excited and convinced. As each individual lawmaker was approached, they each said the same thing. *"I believe it personally, but I think you will find I am alone. No one else will go for it. It will never fly."* Of course, once they found out that their colleagues were of the same mind, they came out of the closet and began backing it.

Dr. John Hagelin

The plan was put to the government and to private parties by Dr. John Hagelin, who was the Natural Law candidate in the last presidential election. John Hagelin is a world authority in unified quantum field theories. His writings on electroweak unification, grand unification, supersymmetry and cosmology include some of the most cited references in the physical sciences. He has conducted pioneering work at the forefront of theoretical physics at the European Center for Particle Physics and Stanford Linear Accelerator Center and is responsible for the development of a highly successful grand unified theory based on the superstring. As you can see, he is no lightweight.

For a lot more of the details of this plan and exactly who in the government and elsewhere is supporting it, go to *www.permanentpeace.org.*

The Maharishi Effect

The plan is based on the scientifically proven phenomena known as the Maharishi effect. You may well have heard of

Maharishi Mahesh Yogi. He was the man who left India almost fifty years ago to teach Transcendental Meditation (TM) to westerners *(most notably the Beatles),* and to demonstrate to the scientific community that meditation has benefits that can be scientifically proven.

Whether you think he runs a cult or not, or is a little weird or just plain cuckoo, doesn't matter one jot. It's not about him. It's about the science and it's about the potential of that science to bring about peace.

His scientists have proved the power of meditation to the full satisfaction of the scientific community and he continues to attract large funds from the National Institute of Health for more studies. During the last 25 years they have focussed on the benefits of large-group meditations, studying the extent to which such events create peace in the society at large.

The Proof

A number of experiments were undertaken during that time which show conclusively that when a significant number of people in a given city meditate together over a period of time, a pattern of social coherence is created in the population such that social stress is reduced and crime rates go down quite significantly.

It was shown in a study of 160 cities that as the number of people meditating increased or decreased over a period of seven years, so the crime rate went up and down in the same proportion with all other factors statistically controlled for.

There have also been numerous studies that have shown that when this approach is used in war torn areas like the Middle East, TM is effective in quelling violence and open warfare. A day-by-day study of a two month vigil in Israel during which meditators came and went showed that on days when the numbers were high, deaths in neighboring Lebanon dropped by 76%. These results were replicated in seven consecutive experiments over a two year period during the peak of the Lebanon War.

As I have observed myself when we do the Radical Forgiveness work in large groups, there is an increase in the overall effect as the group size grows. As more and more people enter a state of consciousness that gives them access to the Unified Field *(defined by quantum mechanical theories as "the fountainhead of all the laws of nature — the ultimate source of all order displayed throughout the Universe")*, there is a greater tendency for people in the locality to experience effects similar to those experienced by the person doing the forgiveness work.

How Many People?

The research shows that the intensity or power grows as the square of the number of participants. (N squared). This means that a relatively small number of people engaging in the spiritual practices that give access to the Unified Field can have a global effect.

Gregg Braden in his book, The Isaiah Effect, quotes a mathematician who says that if the square root of 1% of the entire population of the world all together and at the same time took part some kind of spiritual technology that accessed the Unified Field, a global shift in consciousness would occur. That number turns out to be a mere 880,000 people.

The Invincible Defense Technology, which is the name now given to the Maharishi project based on Transcendental Meditation, is even more precise. Based on the effects of the studies referred to earlier, they calculate that if they have 40,000 people all meditating together in a single location world peace would occur.

The plan that they are putting to the government calls for financial support in locating and sustaining for a long period of time 40,000 meditators somewhere in the world. Their sole purpose would be to stay connected to the Unified Field and stimulate and enliven UNITY and PEACE in the collective consciousness of the world.

The Consciousness Factor

David Hawkins, MD., Ph.D., in his groundbreaking book "Power vs. Force," shows quite conclusively that the power that an individual has to change the world — for better or worse — depends on his or her level of consciousness.

The number required to make a difference, therefore, is determined by the consciousness of those involved. The higher their consciousness, the fewer it will take — and the effect is exponential. He shows that having even a tiny number of people with a high level of consciousness involved can dramatically reduce the overall number required to bring PEACE to the world.

Hawkins has a very refined and scientifically validated scale of consciousness that is measured according to the principles to which an individual is totally committed and by which he or she consistently lives. For example, a person who is unkind, vengeful, mean or despising of others — or blames everyone else for their unhappiness — will have a very low level of consciousness. Someone who is forgiving, kind, merciful and accountable for his/her own life, will carry a high level of consciousness.

Someone who has a relatively low level of consciousness will have a negative effect on the world but insofar as their power as an individual is negligible *(with the exception of a few individuals who perversely rule with force or in some other way affect mass consciousness is such a way as to drag it down),* it only matters when such a consciousness is shared by millions of others.

That being the case at this present time, were it not for the fact that mass negative energy is counterbalanced by only a very few people with a high level of consciousness, there would be very little hope for humanity. As Hawkins himself says, "But for these counterbalances, mankind would self-destruct out of the sheer mass of its unopposed negativity."

[By the way, it is important that we not make any judgments about all this. As Harley pointed out in the story, everyone is where they need to be. It might well be that in order for those who aspire to a higher consciousness to reach a new level, they might need that mass consciousness against which to push].

The good news is however, as Hawkins shows, since the effect that consciousness can have on the creation of reality increases exponentially the higher up the scale a person goes, a very few people holding the higher vibration can counterbalance the millions who are at the lower end of that scale.

The Critical Level of Consciousness

Hawkins gives a scale of 1 - 1000 and identifies 200 as being the critical point of consciousness where a person puts back as much energy into the world as they take out. Below 200 a person drains energy from the collective and the net effect is negative. Above 200, a person's contribution is positive.

The Shift Has Occurred

For those of us who have been intuiting a general raising of consciousness since the harmonic convergence, Hawkins has it confirmed. He tells us, *"The collective level of consciousness of mankind remained 190 for many centuries and, curiously, only jumped to its current level of 207 within the last decade."* Bearing in mind that under 200 creates a net loss of power while over 200 creates a net gain, that represents quite a breakthrough in mass consciousness.

The Counterbalancing Effect

While 85% of the population of the world calibrates well below the level of 200, it is the counterbalancing power of the relatively few individuals near the top that brings the average to 207. He points out that only 4% of the population calibrates at 500 and above; only 0.4% reach 540 and a level of consciousness calibrating at 600 or above is only reached by 1 in 10 million.

Hawkin's testing shows that one person vibrating at level 300 will counterbalance 90,000 individuals below 200. Someone at the level of 400 counterbalances 400,000 people below 200 while someone at the level of 500 counterbalances 750,000 individuals at less than 200. One individual at 600 counterbalances 10 million people under 200.

Our Own Level

You need to read Hawkin's book to get a good feel for where you might be but I would say that the very fact that you have this book in your hands and find yourself aligned with it, would suggest that you are in the range somewhere between 300 and 350—perhaps even on the cusp of the critical change of consciousness which Hawkins says happens at 350. At that level individuals become aware that they are the source and creator of their life experience and develop the capacity to live harmoniously with the forces of life. That is to say, they have integrated and have begun to live Radical Forgiveness as their 'default' way of life. *(See Evolution of Consciousness Chart on the very last page of this book).*

The Power of YOU

If that is so, that would mean that if you are able to hold the vibration of Radical Forgiveness the whole time and nurture only thoughts of PEACE, LOVE in the awareness of the PERFECTION of what is occurring out there in the world, you could be in effect counterbalancing approximately 200,000 people who might be in fear, anger, apathy and despair. Given that we have 237 million people in the U.S., it would only take around 2,000 people at the 350 level holding the vibration of PEACE to tip the scales in that direction.

However, let's assume that you are not able to consistently emanate PEACE and LOVE and be in the vibration of Radical Forgiveness all the time and that you are closer to the 300 level. You would still be counterbalancing 90,000 individuals below 200. That would mean tipping the balance towards PEACE in the U.S. would require only 2,633 people.

A Question of Focus

As you can see, these numbers are not large. The problem is not numbers; rather it is a question of raising consciousness and aligning that energy so that it is focussed like a laser beam. The Radical Forgiveness technology will help us do that, especially if, at certain moments in time, sufficient numbers of people who have already integrated Radical Forgiveness into their beingness, do something as a group, all at the same time. It is in our plan to create these opportunities.

Even if we bear in mind that, as Hawkins says that, on average, people only shift around five points in their lifetime, I am quite certain in my own mind that engaging in the Radical Forgiveness technology will enable us to shift considerably more than that. Even if it only enables us to spike at a considerably higher level for a short period of time, if a number of us were able to do it all at the same time, the effect would be dramatic.

Saddam Gets Off the Hook

I witnessed at first hand how the power of group focus can change 'negative' energy. In November of 1998, I was a speaker at a Universal Lightworker's Conference in Florida and while there, participated in event that literally prevented an outbreak of war between the US and Iraq.

My friends, Gregg Braden and James Twyman, both of whom were also speakers at the conference, had organized a world-wide internet-based peace meditation that they would anchor at the conference at 10:00 PM on the Saturday night. Because of the three months of internet activity, many millions of people would be holding peace in their hearts at that time as a general expression of desire for peace in the world.

As it happened though, this was the very day that President Clinton ordered the dispatch of hundreds of aircraft fully armed with bombs and missiles to go and severely punish Saddam Hussein for having frustrated the US effort to bring about the dissolution within Iraq of weapons of mass destruction.

As we began the meditation at 10:00 PM, the aircraft were in the air, en-route to Iraq. Even then, we did not meditate on there being no war. That would have been an attachment to an outcome and therefore an attempt to control. We simply meditated on finding peace in our own hearts and maintaining it no matter what happened. If it was meant to be that the US and Iraq had to be at war with each other, so be it. Who were we to say that it should not be? Besides that, being *against* something only adds to the energy. Being against war only increases its likelihood. Clearly, our job was to maintain the energy of peace, nothing more, nothing less. We did this to the best of our ability—along with millions all around the world.

After the meditation which lasted no more than 15 minutes, we went on to something else—dancing if I recall correctly. At 12:15 AM, Gregg Braden came back into the room and announced that a bulletin had given the news that Saddam Hussein had capitulated and that as a consequence President Clinton had ordered the aircraft to turn around and come home. There would be no war.

What needs to be clearly understood is that there was no war that day because a sufficient number of people around the world had together, at one moment in time, accessed the unified field and created a pattern of coherence (peace) in the outer world which was purely a reflection of the peace that each individual created within him/herself.

When we come together in this way and focus our spiritual energy on peace, we see that we are no longer restricted to being the effect under the law of cause and effect. Instead, we become the cause.

This is exactly what underlies the Radical Forgiveness technology. When you do a Radical Forgiveness worksheet, either on paper or using the on-line version from our web site, you access the Unified Field of Consciousness. The worksheet enables you to create a coherent pattern of forgiveness through which all the energy tied up in blame, resentment, righteousness, anger, fear, etc., is automatically released. You don't need to understand how it works and you don't have to know what the unconscious energy patterns actually contain. In fact, it's so easy, it's hard to imagine that it could have so much effect—but it manifestly does.

[**Note:** *In hindsight, we now realize that Saddam was doing what he had always done; given in just enough to* *ensure his survival — no more no less. Some would say now that we should have finished him off then, just as we should have finished him off after Desert Storm. You might even say that our meditation not only saved the day for him because it gave him a break in the energy of aggression, but that we contributed to the need to have the current war. In that sense our meditation was counterproductive. Maybe so. But if we see it from the standpoint of the spiritual big picture and the idea contained in the story of Harley and Jack, it was all perfect. It all added to the drama that is now unfolding. If the effort by Clinton to bring Saddam to heel had resulted in Saddam's death or overthrow, it would have thwarted the plan for America's healing and the Awakening.]*

Twyman's ' Research

James Twyman is continuing to produce these kinds of effects through mass prayer vigils over the internet. He has also found some interesting ways to scientifically validate the effects.

Early in 2003, Jimmy went to Israel and held several prayer vigils there, in person, while simultaneously having people participate over the internet at certain appointed times.

Fortunately for him, the Israeli Military keeps a precise record of every event that occurs each day and they were very willing to provide those records so he could see whether the focussed prayer experiments made any difference.

The statistics showed a dramatic drop in the number of incidents that occurred in both Israel and Palestine on the day following the vigil. For example, the number of shots fired at military installations dropped by at least 50% and other violent acts dropped by 100%. They did go back up the day after the vigil, but the power of focussed prayer was clearly demonstrated with significant statistics to prove it.

The Invincible Defence Technology Project has shown that this improvement can be sustained over time if there are sufficiently large numbers of people permanently engaged. Jimmy is developing programs that will have the same effect and we are doing the same thing with Radical Forgiveness.

Could this be what 9/11 was really all about? Was the Divine purpose, as was suggested in the story, to humble the U.S. and other countries that have dominated the world for years to the point where they would finally turn to the truth that *'our power lies in our defenselessness?'*

Could it be that we are indeed arriving at a point where we are beginning to realize that the only politics that works are ***spiritual politics*** based on spiritual law *(as opposed to the politics of greed, power, and control of others)?*

Could it be that we are coming to understand that the most powerful force in the Universe, far more powerful than the nuclear force — is the power of PEACE and that we have found the means to access it and gift it to the world?

If so, the case might well be made that Osama bin Laden was instrumental in bringing about the very breakthrough in consciousness that we have all been praying for.

29: The Bridge to Peace

I had always known intuitively that, since, according to spiritual principle, means and ends are inseparable, the key to world peace would have to be a technology of consciousness. That means, as Ghandi most effectively demonstrated, that if we want peace we must BE peace.

Radical Forgiveness is just such a technology. It is a technology of consciousness that can truly bring us to a place of inner peace. It can also help us to maintain peace even in circumstances that are anything but peaceful.

As we saw in the last chapter, if enough people use it and focus their energy through its use, it has the potential to change mass consciousness and, if done in sufficient numbers, bring about world peace.

My mission statement, formulated back in 1997, is ***"to raise the consciousness of the planet through Radical Forgiveness and to create a world of forgiveness by 2012."***

I must say that—pre Harley—I had always thought that we as individuals would have to create a world of forgiveness without the help of our so-called leaders; that it would essentially be a bottom up approach with little or no help coming from the top, especially the governments and Institutions of State.

I have always felt, and still hold to this point of view, that world peace is a spiritual issue—not a political one—and that the spiritual shift that we are looking for will come about as a consequence of individuals choosing to let go of fear and greed in favor of PEACE and LOVE.

That said, politicians are individuals, too, and each of them will be at choice no less than anyone else with every bit as much to lose or gain. George W. Bush is no exception.

Having briefly become acquainted with the idea that there is sound scientific evidence for the existence of a range of consciousness technologies and that the government has shown interest in them, we might now look back and see how this might tie into 'Jack's Story.'

The first point is that, whereas previously it seemed ridiculous to even imagine that George Bush would awaken and lead the world into a spiritual revolution, it is now perhaps not totally inconceivable that a President might one day actually use it as an instrument of policy. Wouldn't that be something?

What might we do with this insight? How might we empower the idea to the extent that it could actually occur?

Well, for a start, I for one am going to stop sneering and sniping at George Bush at every opportunity and I am going to imagine him as 'Jack'. I am going to hold it that he is indeed that soul on a mission to heal America and awaken the world. I am going to align my energy with his and hold that vision. Why not?

Nothing would please me more than to witness his Awakening and be part of the world that he might create. My not being open to that possibility creates a block against its happening. So why not hold that vision for him? It will cost me nothing but my self-righteousness and need to judge.

Whereas I have, up to now, seen all the stupid errors and slips that he has made as a vindication of my self-righteous judgments about him and have taken pleasure in his having made them, I will now see them as Harley described them—as being absolutely necessary to the mission. I will now see all his seemingly bad mistakes as being in the service of creating the conditions where the spiritual solution becomes necessary and the Awakening occurs.

Whereas up to now I have been critical of what I have judged to be his totally irresponsible policy decisions, no matter whether it be over the environment, taxes, global warming, economic policy, world trade and foreign policy, etc., I will now see those in that same purposeful light.

Not that I will simply acquiesce to everything he proposes—far from it! But when I argue for my position on any one of those issues and many others besides, I will do so in the full knowledge and comfort that in the end, whatever happens is what is meant to happen and that 'Universal Intelligence' has it handled.

In other words, I will practice Radical Forgiveness with regard to George Bush and all those around him. I will see him as the child of God that he is, with a mission of creating Heaven on Earth — if only we will let him!

How about you? Will you do the same? What the heck — you don't have to tell anyone. ***Just do it!***

I am also going to take Harley at his word about America's healing being dependent on how the dynamic between President Bush and Saddam Hussein plays out and I will help empower the healing process by using the Radical Forgiveness technology myself — because I too have that same shadow. I too am in need of healing what Saddam mirrors for me. You might wish to do the same but first let me explain how this would work.

As you must know by now, it is one of the core assumptions of the Radical Forgiveness technology that what upsets us most about someone represents what we most hate in ourselves and have denied, repressed and projected onto them. Furthermore, that in order to heal and grow we attract such people into our life to mirror our self hatred for us. This gives us an opportunity to recognize that it is a part of ourself that is screaming out for LOVE and acceptance.

As Harley explained it, that was precisely the role Shadeem (Eric) was preparing for when training for his incarnation. His mission was to give Jack the opportunity to recognize that the very things that seemed so dark in Shadeem were mirror images of what was in America's shadow. Once that was recognized by Jack, Shadeem's role would be over and he could leave the scene. America would be healed.

As was hinted at in the story, George Bush Senior obviously didn't recognize the prior opportunity. Neither did Clinton when Milosovic gifted him with the very same chance. And now Saddam is back offering it once again for George W. Bush.

Will he get it this time? Probably not. Does it really matter? Not at all — because as we have stressed before — we are all Jack, which means we can do it ourselves. We don't need the President to do it — we can all heal the soul of America. We have the spiritual technology to do it right at our fingertips — in fact, just one click away.

Go to my web site, ***www.radicalforgiveness.com*** and select **'America's Healing.'** This will take you to a part of site devoted to providing you with a number of online Radical Forgiveness instruments that you can use AT NO CHARGE.

These will include interactive worksheets, declarations, invocations, prayer suggestions, meditations, etc., all of which are designed to help us all hold the vibration of PEACE and LOVE, no matter what is happening 'out there.'

One of the instruments is a forgiveness worksheet on Saddam Hussein. This does not, I hasten to add, ask you to forgive Saddam in the traditional way for all his atrocities and cruel behavior. Absolutely not. In human terms and viewed from the perspective of the World of Humanity, what he has done is unforgivable. In this human world he is both responsible and accountable and he will no doubt pay the price. Traditional forgiveness is all but impossible in cases like this.

However, our forgiveness worksheet does not use traditional forgiveness. It uses Radical Forgiveness. This asks that we suspend our human perception of what is happening in favor of a spiritually informed awareness that beneath the apparent circumstances in this physical world there is a higher purpose being served in what is occurring.

A Radical Forgiveness worksheet asks only that we become willing to open our minds to the possibility that—when seen from the World of Divine Truth—that everything is in Divine Order and that a higher purpose is being served. It does not require belief—only the willingness to try it out and see if it works. We do this by doing the worksheet.

Experience over a number of years shows that it does indeed work in the sense that it enables us to tap into the Unified Field which, as you may recall, enables us to become the CAUSE rather than the EFFECT in the world. In other words, it enables what we would normally conceive of as miracles to occur in the outer experience as a result of our raised consciousness.

In the specific case of Saddam Hussein, the worksheet simply asks us to entertain the possibility that the essence of Jack's story is close to the truth. That is, that Saddam Hussein came into this realm to help heal the soul of America and contribute to the Awakening of Humanity. Our willingness to be open to that possibility contributes to those very processes. And willingness is ALL that is required of us. Belief is not necessary.

Similarly, being the CAUSE in a cause-and-effect world simply by projecting thoughts coming from an elevated consciousness, means that our thoughts about PEACE and LOVE would create those qualities as vibrations and manifest the physical conditions in the world that would support them.

As a result we would see aggression giving way to compassion along with a desire on the part of people to assist each other and cooperate in all areas. Wars would cease and agreements to live together in harmony would get honored. This is the ONLY way to create peace. Nothing else will work.

When we, as a group of people spread around the globe holding the same vibration, use the Radical Forgiveness technology to create PEACE, we will be more powerful than any government, politician, corporate entity, church or world leader. We will be infinitely more powerful than the United Nations has ever been or ever will be — unless it too some day uses this same technology. *(This is not beyond the bounds of possibility. Let us envision the day when it might.)*

We live in a holographic universe. That means that even the smallest part of it, when separated from the main hologram, still contains the whole. That means that you are the soul of America. Everything that America has been or is now, you are — shadow as well. That's why it is possible for you to heal America just by engaging in these simple, consciousness raising activities.

Your involvement will demand very little of your time. The instruments are simple and designed to instantly create a coherent pattern of Radical Forgiveness that resonates with the part of the Unified Field that is in you and in every American person. The effort required is minimal.

You might be asking how something so simple and subtle could possibly change the world? The quantum physicists could explain it to you in great detail using complicated theorems, but I find it easier to use a simple analogy. Homeopathy offers one that works quite well.

A homeopathic remedy is made by putting into a very large amount of pure water a minute drop of the substance that might have upset you in the first place, the principle being that 'like heals like.' Then a tiny amount of that water is taken out and put into another very large batch of pure water. This is repeated over and over, the idea being to dilute the mixture to the point where, if you put it under the microscope, there would be absolutely no trace of the rogue substance present. Paradoxically, the more diluted it is the more potent it is. What remains is the subtle but coherent energetic imprint of the original substance. The body recognizes the energetic pattern and uses that information to balance itself naturally. This is clearly a very subtle but extremely potent process.

Just as a skeptic would say that, since nothing can be found in the water, a homeopathic remedy is simply a hoax, so would a skeptic say that it is simply ridiculous to claim that something so simple and so seemingly insignificant as a Radical Forgiveness worksheet on Saddam Hussein could heal the soul of America.

Yet, homeopathic medicine has been around for more than 5,000 years. If it had been ineffective it would have disappeared a long time ago, along with leeches. Homeopathy is infinitely more effective than allopathic medical practice in curing chronic illness. Just because something is subtle, doesn't mean that it doesn't have potency.

In the same way, the Radical Forgiveness technology works precisely because it is so subtle and so easy to do. It requires little of the person doing it—just a tiny amount of willingness to entertain the possibility that everything is purposeful. It requires no special training, no special knowledge and no discipline other than to make the effort to spend a few moments doing a worksheet, meditating on a declaration or using whatever other of the instruments provided in the package feels right in that moment. That means that virtually anyone can do it. Therefore, it shouldn't be too difficult to get sufficient numbers of people around the world engaged to create a CAUSE strong enough to overcome the present fear-based consciousness and create the healing.

There is also a built-in, self-oriented motivation to engage in this work—the benefits to the individual are enormous. Radical Forgiveness changes peoples' lives—there is no doubt about that. However, the principle of the hologram shows that whole contains the parts and vise versa. This means that America's shadow is the individual's shadow too, and each person stands in as much need of healing as America itself. Using the technology will benefit both.

When you use the Radical Forgiveness instruments, notice how you feel afterwards. You will almost certainly feel lighter indicating that some of the weight of America's past has been lifted from your shoulders as well as from your own. Look out too for some miracles occurring in your life.

Even when doing the worksheet on Saddam, by releasing the energy tied up in situations in your own life where someone other than Saddam Hussein might have been mirroring your self-hatred—even though you weren't aware of it while doing the worksheet—all sorts of amazing things will happen.

Now, what about the Awakening? The fantasy made it seem that in order to make the Awakening happen, it would take someone with the power of the President of the United States to do it. We know now that is not the truth. As I have said before, the real message of the story is that we are ALL Jack and it is up to us to awaken to the truth of who we are.

Each of us is able to do this without being an expert in anything. You and I can be fully engaged in this fantastic transformation simply by engaging in the processes alluded to above. The Radical Forgiveness technology is a consciousness raising technology in and of itself and it will create the Awakening. For the first time ever it seems, individuals now have an opportunity to change the world. If we focus our efforts together it will become a matter of certainty.

I believe that 911 and the complex drama being played out in its wake, including the war in Iraq and its aftermath, and/or troubles with Iran, North Korea or whomever— is the single most important event in the history of humanity.

How we *(the human race in its entirety)* respond to all that might happen has implications for our very survival on this planet perhaps, for civilization as we know it most likely, and for our spiritual evolution most definitely.

This is a huge wake up call which I believe has been and is being orchestrated by Spirit to help all of humanity see what we have created and to give us the opportunity to choose again. Those souls who lost their lives on September 11 and since were, I believe, called to serve this great purpose.

Two thousand years ago the effect of our 'not getting it' was not immediately catastrophic—though it has of course proven to be so over time. *(It has actually brought us to this place and situation. If we had heeded Jesus's teachings we would not have the world of hate and separation that we have created. We might well have had Heaven on Earth by now).*

If we fail this time, however, the effects are likely to be immediate, global in scope and catastrophic in nature. This could be our last chance to get it right and the stakes could not be higher.

Until now it has been almost impossible to physically bring huge numbers of people together in common cause. Imagine trying to get in excess of 880,000 people together in one place to do something. Now, with the Internet at our disposal it has become incredibly easy.

This program to create Heaven on Earth will be almost entirely a "web-centric" cyber project. Our web site will be a place to come to use the Radical Forgiveness technology to clear the fear-based material from our own shadows. The interactive on-line program for doing that is already up and running. We are adding other on-line interactive programs such as a 21-day program for forgiving your parents, a self-forgiveness online program, plus workshops and seminars.

We will also be creating and supporting study groups and consciousness circles that focus on holding the vibration of PEACE and LOVE and we shall be publishing a regular newsletter.

The content of the web site will be ever-changing in response to changes in the unfolding drama. As events occur that otherwise might return us to a fear vibration we will provide appropriate instruments to help us maintain our centeredness and PEACE vibration.

I am writing this on the eve of America's unleashing its military power onto Iraq. Clearly, by the time you get this book, the war phase will be over and Saddam Hussein will probably be dead. None of that will matter. Dead or alive, Saddam will continue, in perpetuity, to reflect the American shadow, thereby forever providing America the opportunity to heal itself whenever it chooses to do so.

Who knows what might follow the war and how the drama will continue to play out—or even whether George Bush will still be around when the Awakening finally occurs.

To a very great extent, how long that will take depends on you and me. Just how catastrophic world events need to get before the Awakening occurs also depends, to a very large degree, on you and me.

The choice is ours. We can either go back to sleep and acquiesce to whatever will happen in the way of disasters and cataclysmic events around 2012 as foretold by the wise ones from centuries past and in our present time, or we can take on the awesome responsibility for saving the planet by choosing to awaken.

By coming to our web site and making a commitment to heal yourself first and the world second, you will be contributing energy to the greatest project ever undertaken — to awaken Humanity from its dream and to create Heaven on Earth.

Are You Ready to Help Create 'Heaven on Earth?'

How Could You NOT Want to Be a Part of Something This Important?

Come to

www.radicalforgiveness.com

and
Participate in the Awakening of Humanity
to Itself and the Creation of Heaven
Here on Earth —

The Time is NOW!

"The only failure is the failure to participate."
Buckminster Fuller

Appendix 1

The Assumptions Underlying Radical Forgiveness Technology

Any model which attempts to explain the unexplainable is going to be based on a set of assumptions. For let's be truthful - no one knows who or what God is. It is the great mystery. All we can do is use our minds to the best of our ability and make some assumptions about it. I always say that when we go back into the World of Spirit, we look back on our feeble attempts to understand the spiritual truth of our existence and will laugh ourselves silly.

However, it is not only our theories about God that are based on pure assumption. Many scientific theories are too, Darwin's theory of evolution being a prime example. There's hardly a shred of hard evidence for it, yet it has worked for more than a century as a reasonable model for how nature works and some general principles have been drawn from it. The fact that it has recently come under fire and is being debunked in many quarters as pure nonsense only goes to show how transitory and ephemeral belief systems can be.

Having said all that, the spiritual assumptions underlying Radical Forgiveness are not just plucked out of nowhere. They are very much in step with what physicists know and articulate about the nature of reality - things that the mystics have been saying for many thousands of years.

Indigenous people all around the world have used them for centuries as the basis on which they built their lives. The Native American Indians, the people of Nepal and the Australian Aboriginals come immediately to mind as being possibly the most spiritually advanced peoples in the world as a consequence of making these assumptions central to their lives. And it should be noted that there is surprising correlation in belief between all these peoples.

In the last half century since Einstein came up with his Theory of Relativity and quantum physics surplanted Newtonian physics, science and mysticism have come together. And it has to be said that the mystics have been the ones who have been proved right. Science has come towards mysticism and found it to be true, not the other way round. For those who would like to explore this area more, I would recommend the book by Michael Talbot, "The Holographic Universe."

Assumptions:

1. We live in at least two worlds at the same time and the soul bridges the two and is fully aware of both.

a) The World of Spirit: A spiritual reality - essentially mysterious and beyond our five senses to perceive it and beyond our mental capacity to comprehend it.

b) The World of Humanity: The objective reality that we see "out there" with our five senses. It is the setting in which we live our everyday lives as ***SPIRITUAL BEINGS HAVING A HUMAN EXPERIENCE; i.e. A Feeling Experience***

For the vast majority of the time, our personality self is only aware of the World of Humanity — the world we know and experience through our five senses and extensions thereof such as microscopes and other instruments. It is the setting in which we live our everyday lives. It is a world of physical form, duality, separation, time and space, change and uncertainty.

The World of Spirit is the world of spiritual reality and inner experience. Essentially, it exists as a world without form, changeless, formless, without time, space or separation.

These two worlds are not geographically distinct. They are not places at all, of course, just different frequencies. This accounts for how we exist in both worlds at the same time. It is simply a matter of adjusting our receiver (our body/mind) in such a way as to receive a wider range of frequencies. This is what we mean by expanding our awareness.

Making the journey from the World of Spirit to the World of Humanity *(incarnating)*, in order to experience the qualities inherent in the World of Humanity as a means of spiritual growth is a choice that our soul makes. However, in order that the experience be genuine the soul must develop amnesia about the World of Spirit during the incarnation.

2. Life is not just a random set of events without purpose or intelligence. What appears to be haphazard is really the unfoldment of a Divine plan that is totally purposeful in terms of our spiritual growth.

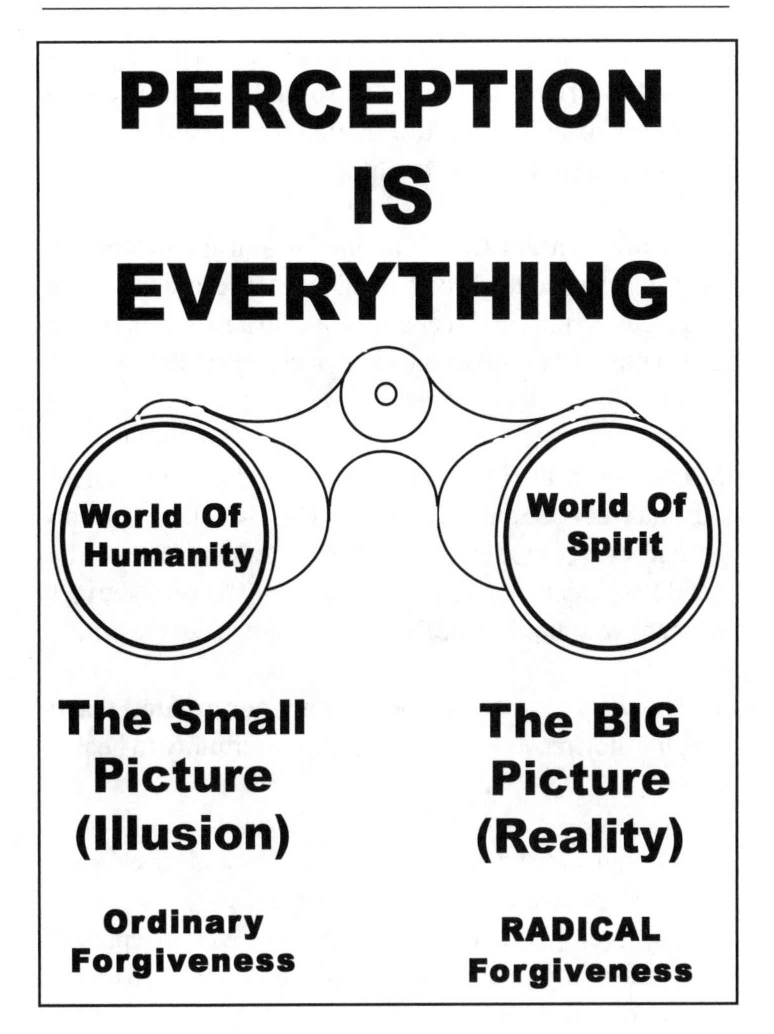

3. We are co-creators with Spirit in the circumstances of our lives and we get precisely what we want (no exceptions). The extent to which we resist (judge) what we get, determines whether we experience it as either joyful or painful.

4. Whenever we get upset with another person (or organization), **they are resonating in us something that we have condemned in ourself and denied, repressed and projected onto that person or thing.**

5. We incarnate with a "mission" — an agreement with Spirit that we would do certain things to meet a karmic debt, complete a "soul level" contract, assist in transforming energies within the human condition, or simply to have experiences.

6. Our soul will always move us in the direction of healing and will keep on creating situations that offer us the opportunity to see the "error" in our thinking or unconscious beliefs. People come into our lives to lovingly "act out" the parts over and over until we heal the error. Herein lies the gift.

7. The people we dislike the most are our greatest teachers, for they may be offering us the opportunity to heal by either:

> **(a)** mirroring what we hate in ourselves and have denied, repressed and projected onto them.
> **(b)** forcing us to look at something we have repressed and which remains as a core belief or unhealed trauma
> **(c)** keeping us on track with our mission.

8. What appears to be happening in the objective world is merely illusion — it is just a projection of our consciousness (our unconscious beliefs, ideas, attitudes, etc). To know what these are, look what is showing up in your life. Life is simply a mirror.

For the full explanation and expansion of these principles and to learn how to raise your consciousness and improve your life, read

'RADICAL Forgiveness

Making Room for the Miracle'

by Colin Tipping
Available in bookstores or from
www.radicalforgiveness.com

"I LOVE This Book!"

says Caroline Myss, Ph.D.

author of 'Sacred Contracts'

"The most exciting book on forgiveness to come out in a very long time. I have never seen anything so well written and so 'right on the money,' on this topic. I am recommending Radical Forgiveness to everyone."

Neale Donald Walsch

author of 'Conversations With God'

The Evolution Of Consciousness

OLD		*EVOLVING*
Piscean - 3rd Dimensional	vs.	Aquarian - 4th Dimensional
Male Energy - Zeuss & Apollo	vs.	Female energy (Divine Androgeny)
5-sensory human beings	vs.	Multi-sensory human beings
Humans having a spiritual experience	vs.	Spiritual beings having a human experience
Reality based on Newtonian Physics	vs.	Reality based on Quantum physics
Physical universe	vs.	Holographic universe
Physical reality	vs.	Metaphysical realities
Human observers of a world 'out there'.	vs.	Humans as co-creators of reality
Evolution as 'Survival of The Fittest.'	vs.	Evolution as 'Spiritual Advancement.'
Biology & Chemistry	vs.	Bio-energetic fields
Externalized power and control.	vs.	Authentic personal power from within.
Religious dogmas	vs.	Personal spirituality
Stable, fixed institutions.	vs.	Constantly changing organic structures.
Rational scientific thought	vs.	Intuitive, open-ended thought
Control centered interaction	vs.	Heart centered interaction
Lower four chakras dominant	vs.	Upper four chakras dominant
Allopathic, high-tech medicine	vs.	Holistic, energy-based medicine
Man dominating/controlling Nature	vs.	Nature respected and honored
Personal survival and success in world	vs.	Spiritual purpose and life mission
Singular life	vs.	Reincarnation and karma
Predominance of Personality or EGO	vs.	Predominance of SOUL
• Fear based consciousness	vs.	• Love based consciousness
• Belief in Separateness	vs.	• Belief in Oneness
• Sorrow, shame, indifference	vs.	• Wisdom and caring
• Woundology	vs.	• Intimacy and Healing
• Judges and exploits	vs.	• Accepts as is
• Manipulating/controlling	vs.	• Flows with what is.
Belief that death is real. (mortality)	vs.	Belief that death is illusion. (Immortality)
Belief in scarcity	vs.	Belief in abundance
Belief in danger	vs.	Belief in safety
Coincidence	vs.	Synchronicity
Investment in the physical illusion	vs.	Trust in the symbolic meaning of events
Victim consciousness	vs.	Forgiveness consciousness
Socially controlled choices	vs.	Personal responsbility and conscious choice
Traditional Forgiveness	vs.	**Radical Forgiveness**

PRINTED IN CANADA